Notetaker

MACROECONOMICS: Principles and Tools

Fourth Edition

Arthur O'Sullivan
Steven M. Sheffrin

Fernando Quijano
Yvonne Quijano

Upper Saddle River, New Jersey 07458

VP/Editorial Director: Jeff Shelstad
Executive Editor: David Alexander
Acquisitions Editor: Jon Axelrod
Assistant Editor: Francesca Calogero
Editorial Assistant : Michael Dittamo
Director of Manufacturing: Vincent Scelta
Production Editor & Buyer: Carol O'Rourke
Printer/Binder: Bindrite Graphics

Copyright © 2006 by Pearson Education, Inc., Upper Saddle River, New Jersey, 07458.
Pearson Prentice Hall. All rights reserved. Printed in the United States of America. This publication is protected by Copyright and permission should be obtained from the publisher prior to any prohibited reproduction, storage in a retrieval system, or transmission in any form or by any means, electronic, mechanical, photocopying, recording, or likewise. For information regarding permission(s), write to: Rights and Permissions Department.

This work is protected by United States copyright laws and is provided solely for the use of instructors in teaching their courses and assessing student learning. Dissemination or sale of any part of this work (including on the World Wide Web) will destroy the integrity of the work and is not permitted. The work and materials from it should never be made available to students except by instructors using the accompanying text in their classes. All recipients of this work are expected to abide by these restrictions and to honor the intended pedagogical purposes and the needs of other instructors who rely on these materials.

Pearson Prentice Hall™ is a trademark of Pearson Education, Inc.

10 9 8 7 6 5 4 3 2 1
ISBN 0-13-188132-9

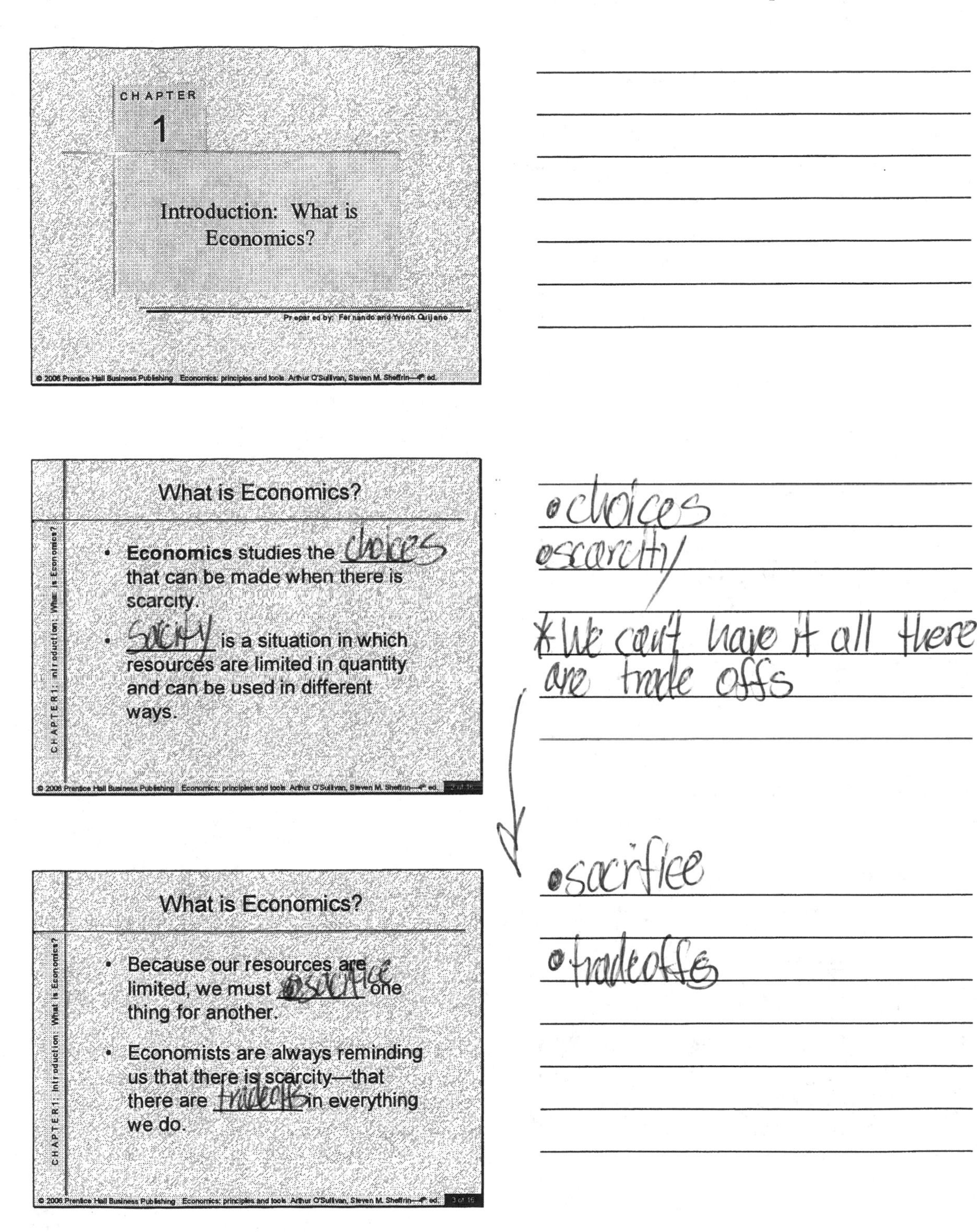
CHAPTER
1
Introduction: What is Economics?
Prepared by: Fernando and Yvonn Quijano
© 2006 Prentice Hall Business Publishing Economics: principles and tools Arthur O'Sullivan, Steven M. Sheffrin—4th ed.
What is Economics?
CHAPTER 1: Introduction: What is Economics?
• Economics studies the choices that can be made when there is scarcity.
• Scarcity is a situation in which resources are limited in quantity and can be used in different ways.
What is Economics?
• Because our resources are limited, we must sacrifice one thing for another.
• Economists are always reminding us that there is scarcity—that there are tradeoffs in everything we do.
• choices
• scarcity
* We can't have it all there are trade offs
• sacrifice
• tradeoffs

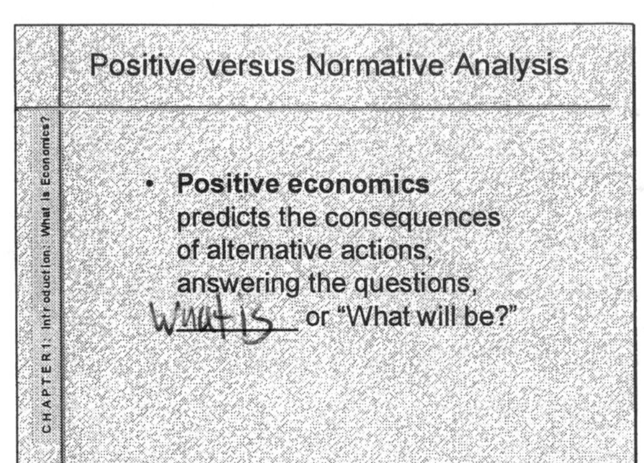

*economics isn't about what to choose, its about understanding tradeoffs in our decision making.
• What is
- about trade offs

Positive versus Normative Analysis

CHAPTER 1: Introduction: What is Economics?

- Normative economics answers the question, What ought to be? Normative questions lie at the heart of policy debates.

© 2006 Prentice Hall Business Publishing Economics: principles and tools Arthur O'Sullivan, Steven M. Sheffrin—4th ed. 5 of 16

*Normative Economics is more about the desion making process itself.

Decisions in a Modern Economy

CHAPTER 1: Introduction: What is Economics?

- Economic decisions are made at every level in society.
- The choices made by individuals, firms, and governments answer three questions:
  1. What products do we produce?
  2. How do we produce the products?
  3. Who consumes the products?

© 2006 Prentice Hall Business Publishing Economics: principles and tools Arthur O'Sullivan, Steven M. Sheffrin—4th ed. 6 of 16

1. What: there are trade offs
2. How: there are alternatives for efficency
3. Who: who to distrubute should government get involved making is possible for the poor to consume more?

Economic Analysis and Modern Problems

- Economic analysis provides important insights into real-world problems.
- Economists attempt to diagnose and solve ________ to problems such as traffic congestion, poverty in Africa, or the problems of an entire economy.

© 2006 Prentice Hall Business Publishing Economics: principles and tools Arthur O'Sullivan, Steven M. Sheffrin—4th ed. 7 of 16

• solve

The Economic Way of Thinking

- The economic way of thinking is best summarized by British economist John Maynard Keynes ________ (1883-1946) as follows:

"The theory of economics does not furnish a body of settled conclusions immediately applicable to policy. It is a method rather than a doctrine, an apparatus of the mind, a technique of thinking which helps its possesor draw correct conclusions."

© 2006 Prentice Hall Business Publishing Economics: principles and tools Arthur O'Sullivan, Steven M. Sheffrin—4th ed. 8 of 16

• Keynes

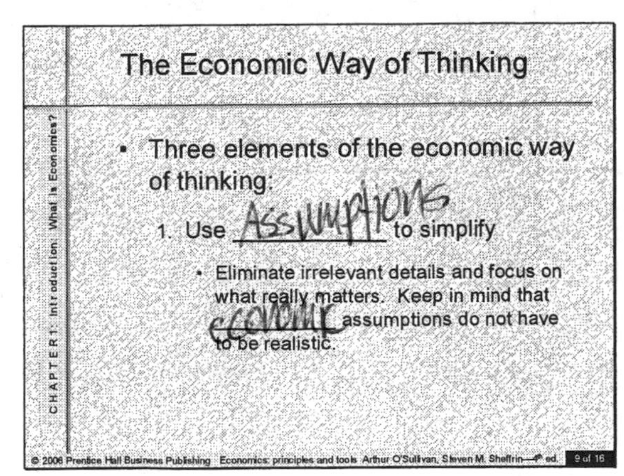

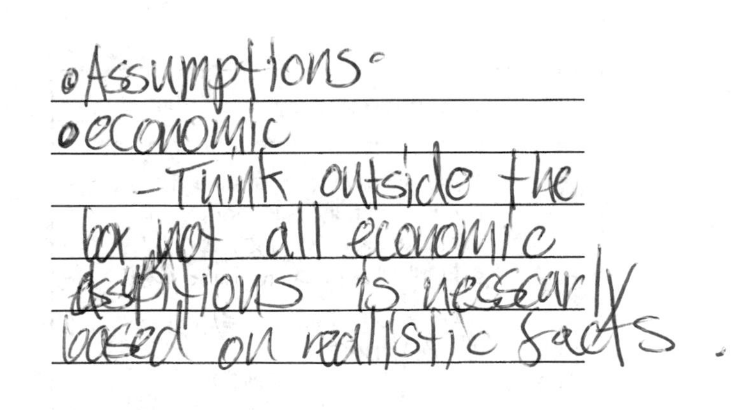

* Economic growth occurs when a country expands its production facilities (machinery & factories) improves it public infrastructure (highways & water systems) widens educational opportunities and adopts new technology.

- Ex. price of apples and the quantity purchased
holding all other variables fixed

The Economic Way of Thinking

- Three elements of the economic way of thinking:
  2. Isolate varbles —Ceteris Paribus
     - Economists are interested in exploring relationships between two variables. A **variable** is a measure of something that can take on different values.
     - The expression Ceteris paribus means that the effect of other tendencies is neglected for a time.

CHAPTER 1: Introduction: What is Economics?

© 2006 Prentice Hall Business Publishing Economics: principles and tools Arthur O'Sullivan, Steven M. Sheffrin—4th ed. 10 of 16

- Variable - is the measure of something that can take on different values
- Ceteris paribus: the Latin expression that other variables are held fixed: "The existence of other tendencies is not denied but their disturbing effect is neglected for a time. The more a issue is narrowed the more exactly can it be handled."

The Economic Way of Thinking

- Three elements of the economic way of thinking:
  3. Think at the Margin
     - A small, one-unit change in value is called a marginal **change**.
     - Economists use the answer to a marginal question as the first step in deciding whether to do more or less of something.

CHAPTER 1: Introduction: What is Economics?

© 2006 Prentice Hall Business Publishing Economics: principles and tools Arthur O'Sullivan, Steven M. Sheffrin—4th ed. 11 of 16

- Think at the margin
- marginal change - small change
  - Marginal questions are used as the first step in deciding whether to do more or less of something

The Economic Way of Thinking

- A key assumption of most economic analysis is that people act rationally, meaning that they act in their own self interest
- Rational people respond to incentives

CHAPTER 1: Introduction: What is Economics?

© 2006 Prentice Hall Business Publishing Economics: principles and tools Arthur O'Sullivan, Steven M. Sheffrin—4th ed. 12 of 16

- Self interest, in economics self interest is more powerful than kindness or altruism. We assume people act in their own interest.
- incentives - people work & change for rewards

- Three elements of economic way of thinking
  - Use Assumptions to simplify
  - Isolate Variables
  - Think by the Margin

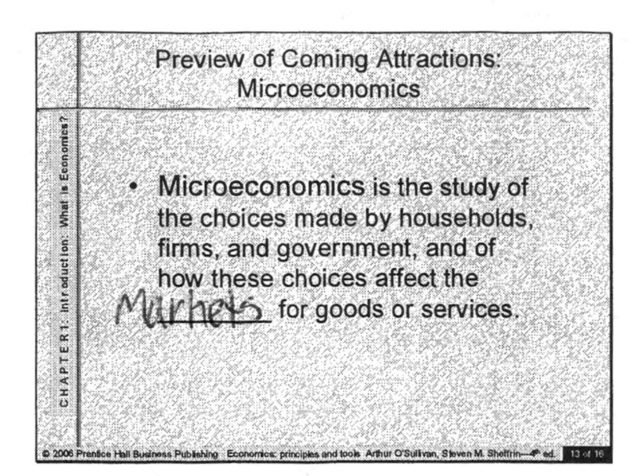

markets

Preview of Coming Attractions: Microeconomics

CHAPTER 1: Introduction: What is Economics?

- We can use microeconomic analysis to:
  1. Understand how markets work and predict changes.
  2. Make personal and managerial decisions.
  3. Evaluate public policies.

© 2006 Prentice Hall Business Publishing Economics: principles and tools Arthur O'Sullivan, Steven M. Sheffrin—4th ed. 14 of 16

• microeconomic analysis

Preview of Coming Attractions: Macroeconomics

CHAPTER 1: Introduction: What is Economics?

- **Macroeconomics** is the study of the nation's economy as a whole.
- We can use macroeconomic analysis to:
  1. Understand why economies grow.
  2. Understand economic fluctuations.
  3. Make informed business decisions.

© 2006 Prentice Hall Business Publishing Economics: principles and tools Arthur O'Sullivan, Steven M. Sheffrin—4th ed. 15 of 16

*economy as a whole

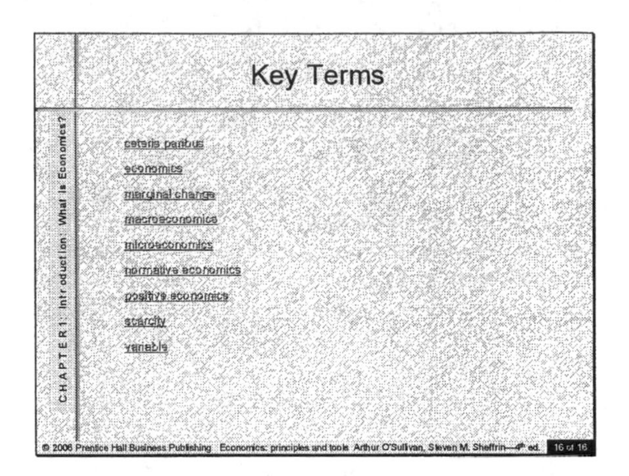
Key Terms
ceteris paribus
economics
marginal change
macroeconomics
microeconomics
normative economics
positive economics
scarcity
variable
CHAPTER 1: Introduction: What Is Economics?
© 2006 Prentice Hall Business Publishing Economics: principles and tools Arthur O'Sullivan, Steven M. Sheffrin—4th ed.
16 of 16

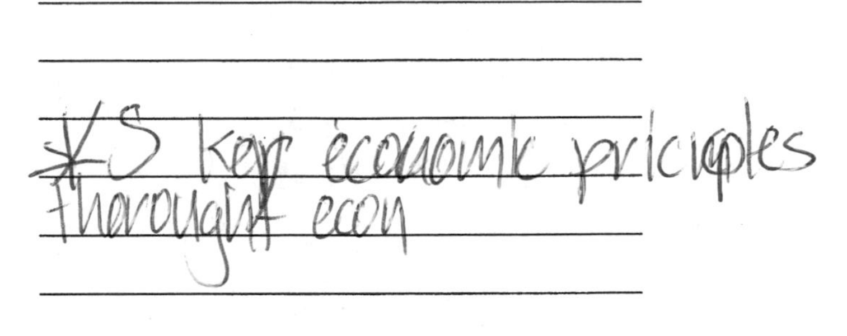

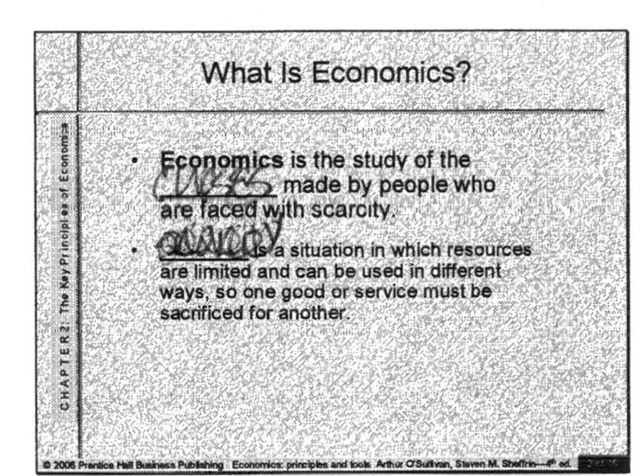

• choices
• opportunity cost (sacrifice, the tradeoff)

The Principle of Opportunity Cost

PRINCIPLE *of Opportunity Cost*
The opportunity cost of something is what you sacrifice to get it.

- Most decisions involve several alternatives. The principle of opportunity cost incorporates the notion of scarcity.
- There is no such thing as a free lunch.

CHAPTER 2: The Key Principles of Economics

© 2006 Prentice Hall Business Publishing Economics: principles and tools Arthur O'Sullivan, Steven M. Sheffrin—4th ed.

• sacrifice

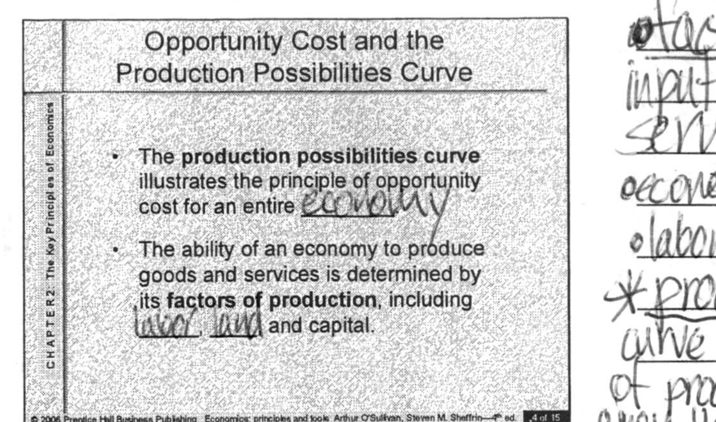

- factors of production is input used to produce goods and services.
- economy
- labor, land

* production possibilities curve - A curve that shows the possible combinations of products that an economy can produce given that its productive resources are fully employed and efficently used.

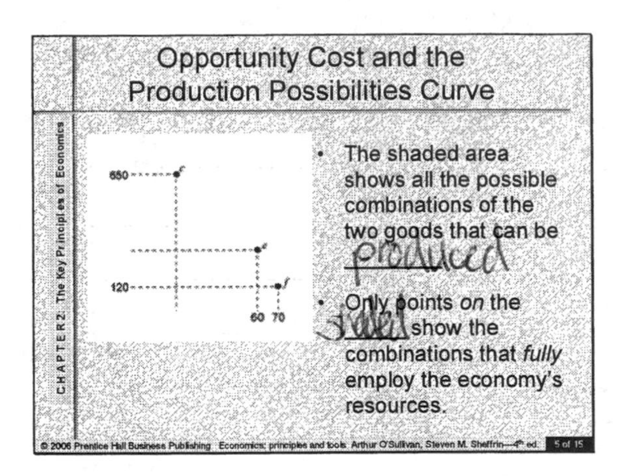

- produce
- shaded area

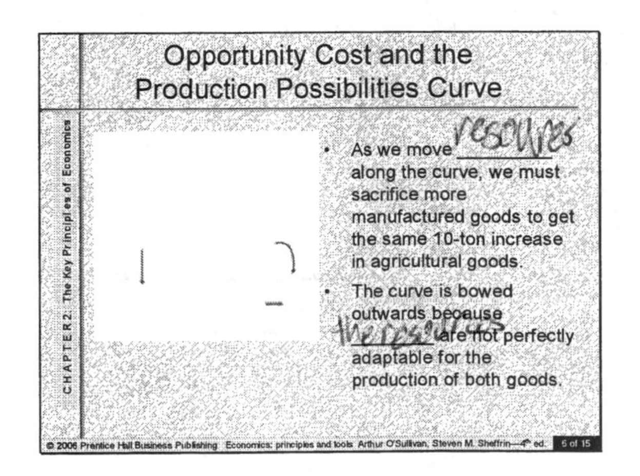

- resoures
- resoures

Opportunity Cost and the Production Possibilities Curve

Initial

- An ________ in the amount of resources available, or a technological innovation, causes the production possibilities to shift outward, allowing us to produce more output with a given quantity of resources.

© 2006 Prentice Hall Business Publishing Economics: principles and tools Arthur O'Sullivan, Steven M. Sheffrin—4th ed.

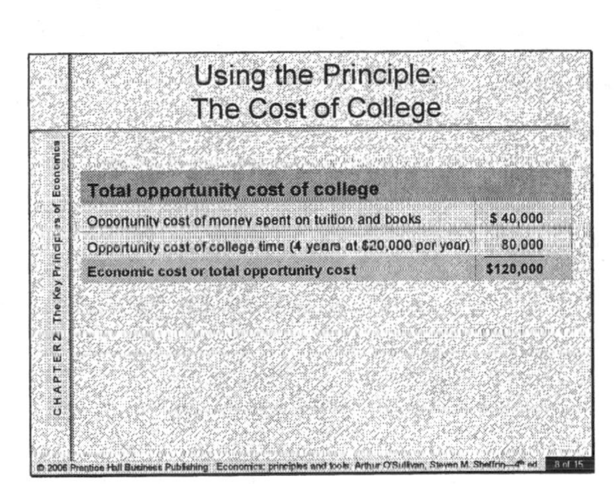

Using the Principle: The Cost of College

Total opportunity cost of college	
Opportunity cost of money spent on tuition and books	$ 40,000
Opportunity cost of college time (4 years at $20,000 per year)	80,000
Economic cost or total opportunity cost	$120,000

© 2006 Prentice Hall Business Publishing Economics: principles and tools Arthur O'Sullivan, Steven M. Sheffrin—4th ed.

The Marginal Principle

Marginal PRINCIPLE

Increase the level of an activity if its marginal benefit ________ its marginal cost; reduce the level of an activity if its marginal cost exceeds its marginal benefit. If possible, pick the level at which the activity's marginal benefit ______ its marginal cost.

© 2006 Prentice Hall Business Publishing Economics: principles and tools Arthur O'Sullivan, Steven M. Sheffrin—4th ed.

The Marginal Principle

CHAPTER 2: The Key Principles of Economics

- When we say **marginal**, we're looking at the effect of only a small, incremental ______.
- The **marginal benefit** of some activity is the _____ benefit resulting from a small increase in the activity.
- The **marginal cost** is the additional cost resulting from a _____ increase in the activity.
- Thinking at the margin enables us to fine-tune our decisions.

© 2006 Prentice Hall Business Publishing Economics: principles and tools Arthur O'Sullivan, Steven M. Sheffrin—4th ed.

Example: How Many Movie Sequels?

CHAPTER 2: The Key Principles of Economics

135

Number of Movies	Marginal Benefit	Marginal Cost
1	$300 million	$125 million
2	$210 million	$150 million

- The marginal benefit _______ the marginal cost for the first two movies, so it is sensible to produce two, but not three movies.

© 2006 Prentice Hall Business Publishing Economics: principles and tools Arthur O'Sullivan, Steven M. Sheffrin—4th ed.

The Principle of Voluntary Exchange

CHAPTER 2: The Key Principles of Economics

> ***PRINCIPLE** of Voluntary Exchange*
> *A voluntary exchange between two people makes both people ______ off.*

- A **market** is an arrangement that allows people to ________ things.
- If participation in a market is voluntary, both the buyer and the seller must be better off as a result of a ___________.

© 2006 Prentice Hall Business Publishing Economics: principles and tools Arthur O'Sullivan, Steven M. Sheffrin—4th ed.

The Principle of Diminishing Returns

***PRINCIPLE** of Diminishing Returns*
Suppose output is produced with two or more inputs and we increase one input while holding the other input or inputs fixed. Beyond some point—called the point of diminishing returns—output will _______ at a decreasing rate.

CHAPTER 2: The Key Principles of Economics

© 2006 Prentice Hall Business Publishing Economics: principles and tools Arthur O'Sullivan, Steven M. Sheffrin—4th ed.

The Real-Nominal Principle

Real-Nominal PRINCIPLE
What matters to people is the real value of money or income—its purchasing power—not the "face" value of money or income.

- The _______ **value** of an amount of money is simply its face value.
- The ____ **value** of an amount of money is measured in terms of the quantity of goods the money can buy.

CHAPTER 2: The Key Principles of Economics

© 2006 Prentice Hall Business Publishing Economics: principles and tools Arthur O'Sullivan, Steven M. Sheffrin—4th ed.

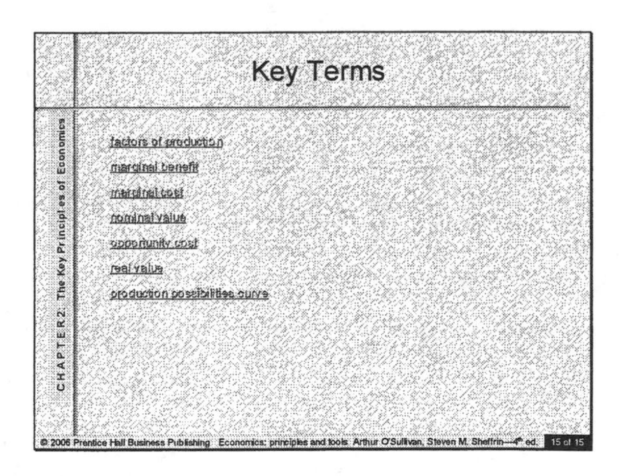

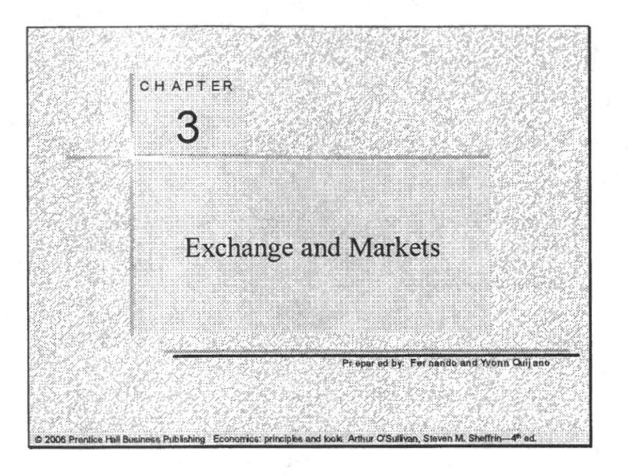

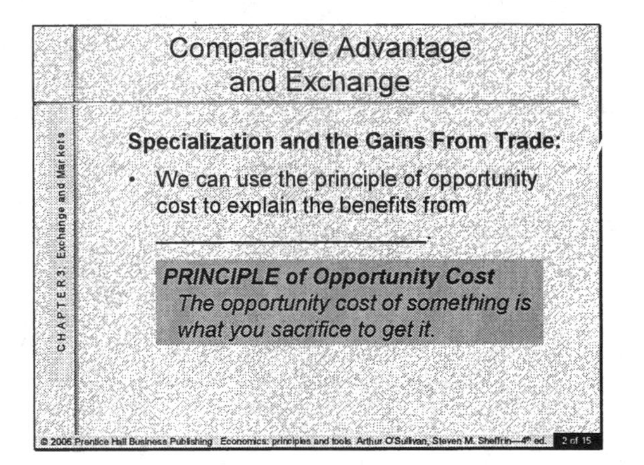

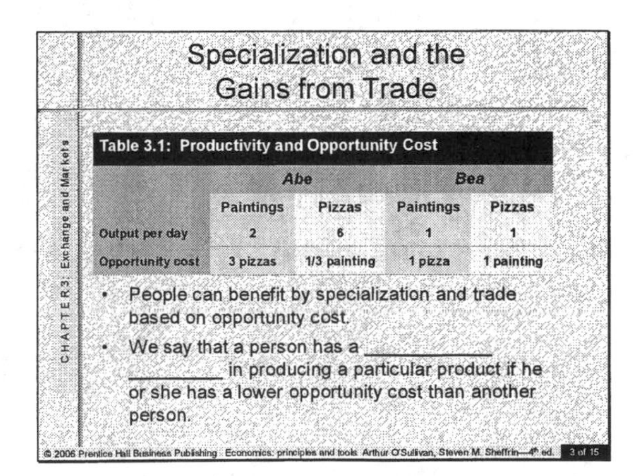

Table 3.1: Productivity and Opportunity Cost

	Abe		Bea	
	Paintings	Pizzas	Paintings	Pizzas
Output per day	2	6	1	1
Opportunity cost	3 pizzas	1/3 painting	1 pizza	1 painting

Specialization and the Gains from Trade

CHAPTER 3: Exchange and Markets

Table 3.2: Specialization, Exchange, and Gains from Trade

	Abe		Bea		Total	
	Paintings per week	Pizzas per week	Paintings per week	Pizzas per week	Paintings per week	Pizzas per week
Abe and Be are self-sufficient	4	24	1	5	5	29
Abe and Bea specialize	0	36	6	0	6	36
After specializing, Abe and Bea exchange 2 pizzas per painting	0 + 5 = 5 (Abe gets 5 painting)	36 – 10 = 26 (Abe gives up 10 pizzas)	6 – 5 = 1 (Bea gives up 5 paintings)	0 + 10 = 10 (Bea gets 10 pizzas)		
Gains from specialization and exchange	1	2	0	5	1	7

© 2006 Prentice Hall Business Publishing Economics: principles and tools Arthur O'Sullivan, Steven M. Sheffrin—4th ed.

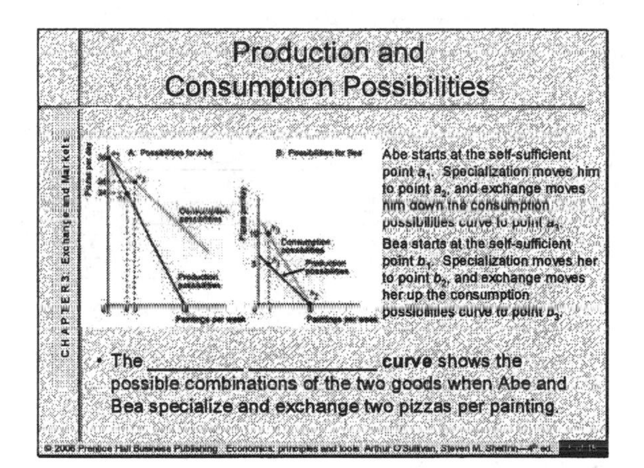

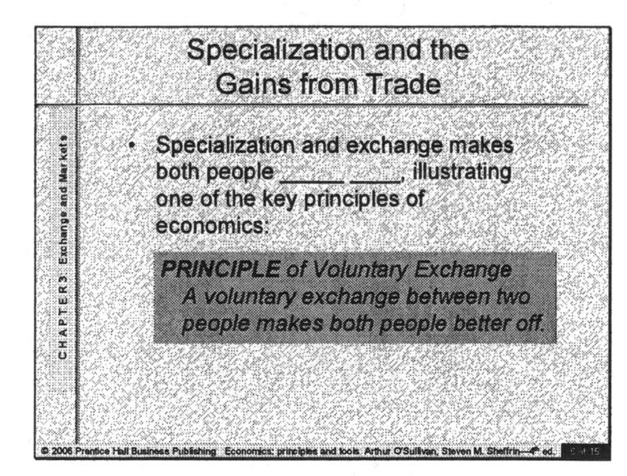

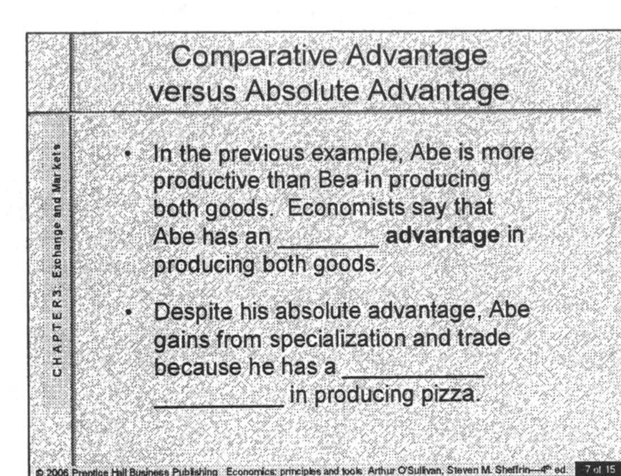

The Division of Labor and Exchange

- Three reasons for productivity to increase with specialization:
  1. Repetition
  2. Continuity
  3. _________
- Specialization and exchange result from differences in _________, which in turn come from differences in innate skills and the benefits associated with the division of labor.

© 2006 Prentice Hall Business Publishing Economics: principles and tools Arthur O'Sullivan, Steven M. Sheffrin—4th ed.

Comparative Advantage and International Trade

- Many people are _________ about the idea that international trade can make everyone better off. Most economists, however, favor international trade. In the words of economist Todd Buchholz:

  "Money may not make the world go round, but money certainly goes around the world. To stop it prevents goods from traveling from where they are produced most inexpensively to where they are desired most deeply."

© 2006 Prentice Hall Business Publishing Economics: principles and tools Arthur O'Sullivan, Steven M. Sheffrin—4th ed.

Markets

CHAPTER 3: Exchange and Markets

- In a _______ _______, people exchange things, trading what they have for what they want.
- Although it appears that markets arose naturally, a number of ______ ________, such as contracts, insurance, patents, and accounting rules, have made them work better.

© 2006 Prentice Hall Business Publishing Economics: principles and tools Arthur O'Sullivan, Steven M. Sheffrin—4th ed.

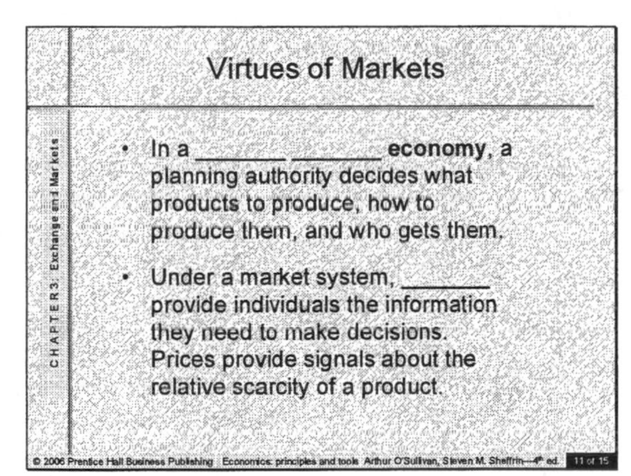

Virtues of Markets

CHAPTER 3: Exchange and Markets

- The decisions made in markets result from the ___________ of millions of people, each motivated by their own interests.
- Adam Smith used the metaphor of the "_______ _____" to explain that people acting in self-interest may actually promote the interest of society as a whole.

© 2006 Prentice Hall Business Publishing Economics: principles and tools Arthur O'Sullivan, Steven M. Sheffrin—4th ed.

Shortcomings of Markets

CHAPTER 3: Exchange and Markets

- "Market failure" is what happens when markets fail to produce the ______ ________ outcomes on their own. The role of government is to correct this problem.
- Market failure can also occur when buyers and sellers have ________ __________ about the quality of goods and services they are exchanging.

© 2006 Prentice Hall Business Publishing Economics: principles and tools Arthur O'Sullivan, Steven M. Sheffrin—4th ed. 13 of 15

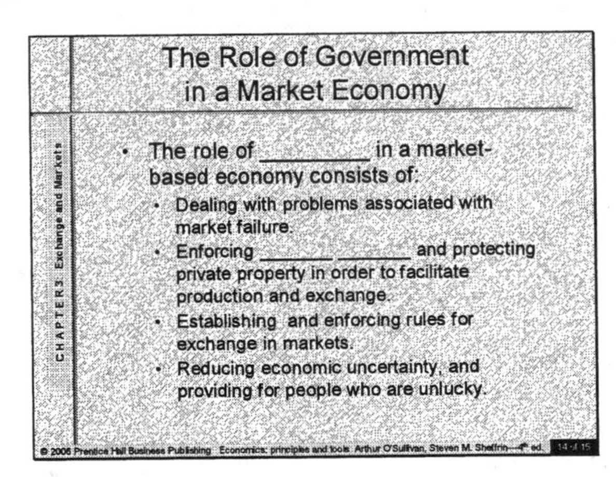

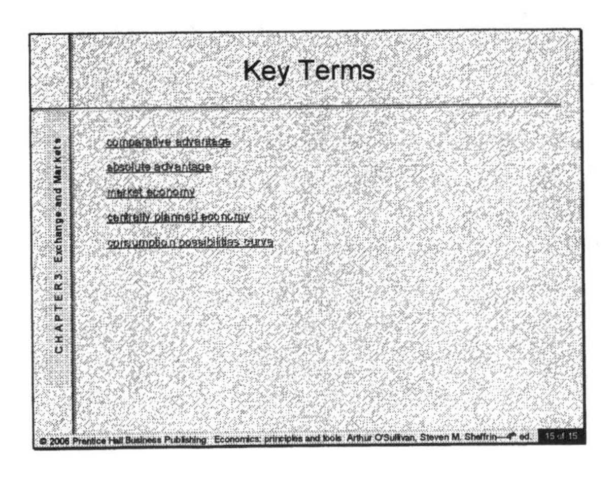

Perfectly Competitive Market

CHAPTER 4: Supply, Demand, and Market Equilibrium

- We use the model of supply and demand—the most important tool of economic analysis—to see how _______ work.
- The model of supply and demand explains how a _________ competitive market operates.
  - A **perfectly competitive market** is a market that has a very _____ number of firms, each of which produces the same standardized product in amounts so small that no individual firm can affect the market price.

© 2006 Prentice Hall Business Publishing Economics: principles and tools Arthur O'Sullivan, Steven M. Sheffrin—4th ed.

The Demand Curve

CHAPTER 4: Supply, Demand, and Market Equilibrium

- Here is a list of variables that affect the individual consumer's decision, using the pizza market as an example:
  - The _____ of the product, for example, the price of pizza
  - The consumer's ______
  - The price of __________ goods such as tacos or sandwiches

© 2006 Prentice Hall Business Publishing Economics: principles and tools Arthur O'Sullivan, Steven M. Sheffrin—4th ed.

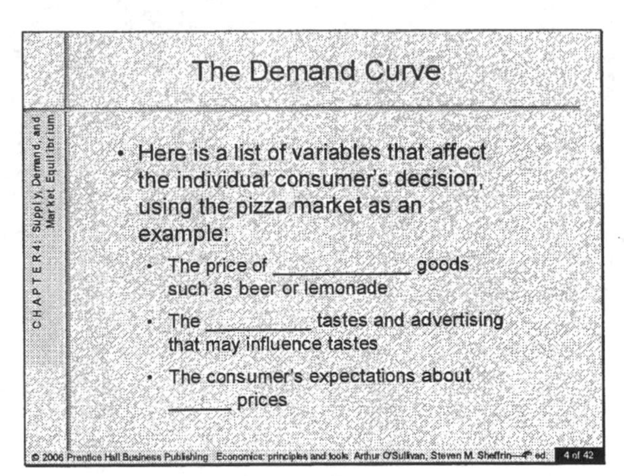

The Individual Demand Curve and the Law of Demand

CHAPTER 4: Supply, Demand, and Market Equilibrium

Table 4.1 Al's Demand Schedule for Pizza

Price	Quantity of pizzas per month
$2	13
4	10
6	7
8	4
10	1

- The **demand schedule** is a table that shows the relationship between _____ and ________ demanded by an individual consumer, ceteris paribus (everything else held fixed).

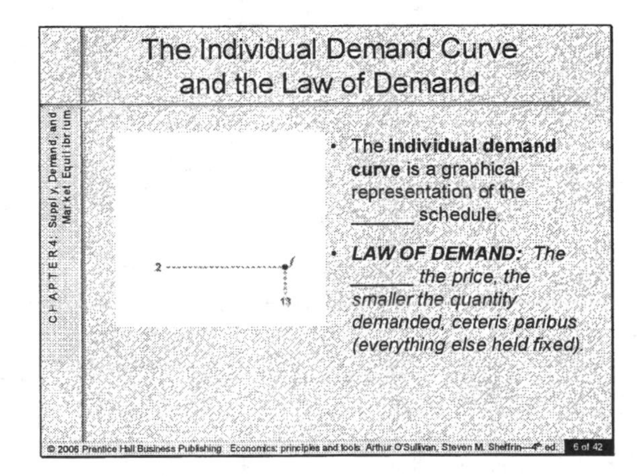

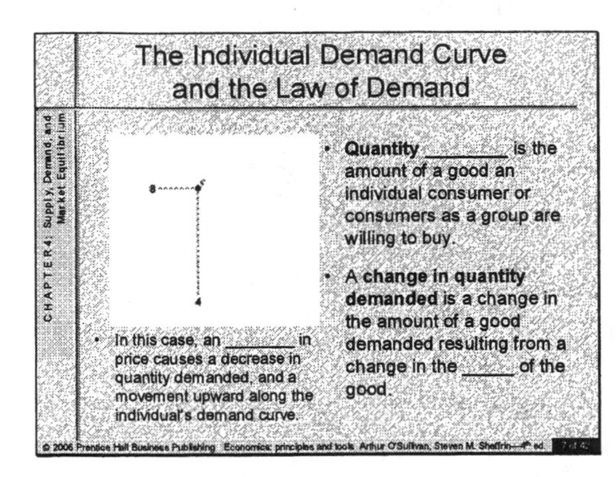

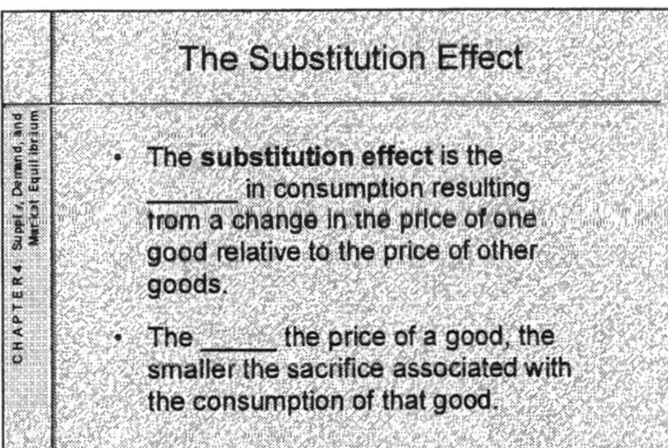

The Income Effect

CHAPTER 4: Supply, Demand, and Market Equilibrium

- The **income effect** describes the change in consumption resulting from an ________ in the consumer's real income, or the income in terms of the goods the money can buy.
- **Real income** is the consumer's _______ measured in terms of the goods it can buy.

© 2006 Prentice Hall Business Publishing Economics: principles and tools Arthur O'Sullivan, Steven M. Sheffrin—4th ed. 9 of 42

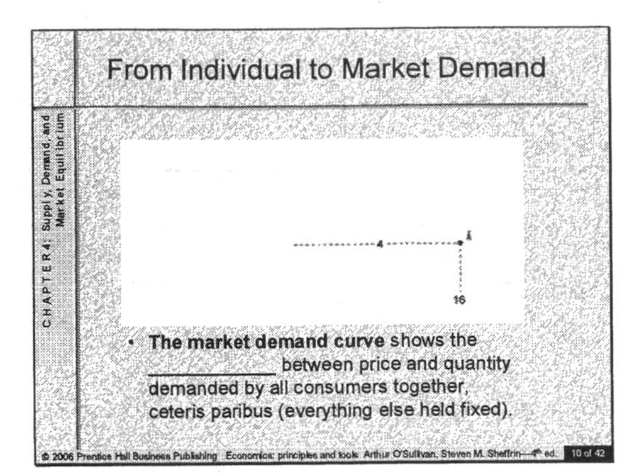

The Supply Curve

CHAPTER 4: Supply, Demand, and Market Equilibrium

- Here are the variables that affect the decisions of sellers, using the market for pizza as an example:
  - The _____ of the product—in this case, the price of pizza.
  - The cost of the ______ used to produce the product, for example, wages paid to workers, the cost of dough and cheese, and the cost of the pizza oven.
  - The state of _________ technology, such as the knowledge used in making pizza.

© 2006 Prentice Hall Business Publishing Economics: principles and tools Arthur O'Sullivan, Steven M. Sheffrin—4th ed. 11 of 42

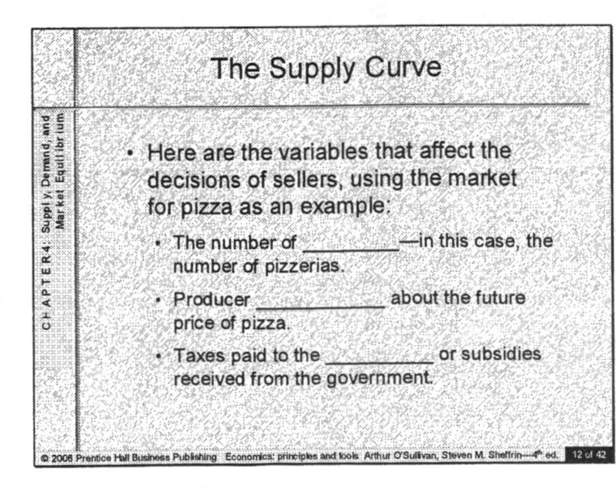

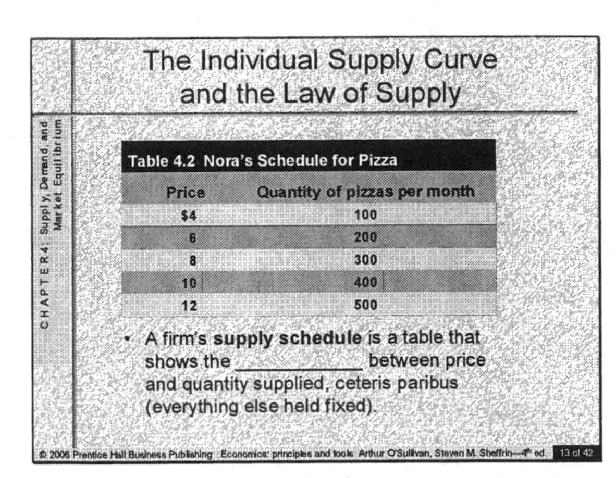

Table 4.2 Nora's Schedule for Pizza

Price	Quantity of pizzas per month
$4	100
6	200
8	300
10	400
12	500

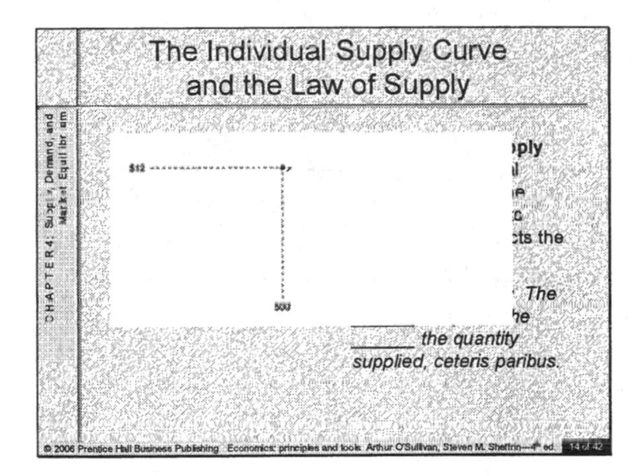

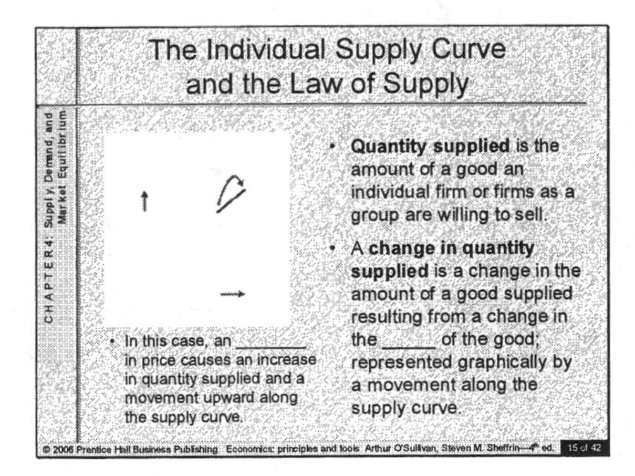

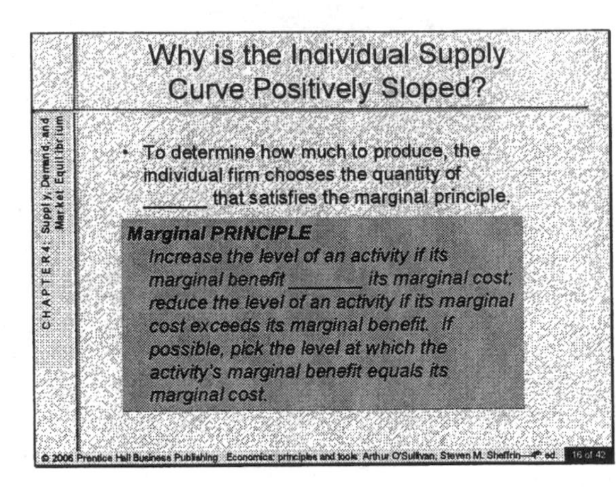
Why is the Individual Supply Curve Positively Sloped?
CHAPTER 4: Supply, Demand, and Market Equilibrium
To determine how much to produce, the individual firm chooses the quantity of ______ that satisfies the marginal principle.
Marginal PRINCIPLE
Increase the level of an activity if its marginal benefit ______ its marginal cost; reduce the level of an activity if its marginal cost exceeds its marginal benefit. If possible, pick the level at which the activity's marginal benefit equals its marginal cost.
© 2006 Prentice Hall Business Publishing Economics: principles and tools Arthur O'Sullivan, Steven M. Sheffrin—4th ed.
16 of 42

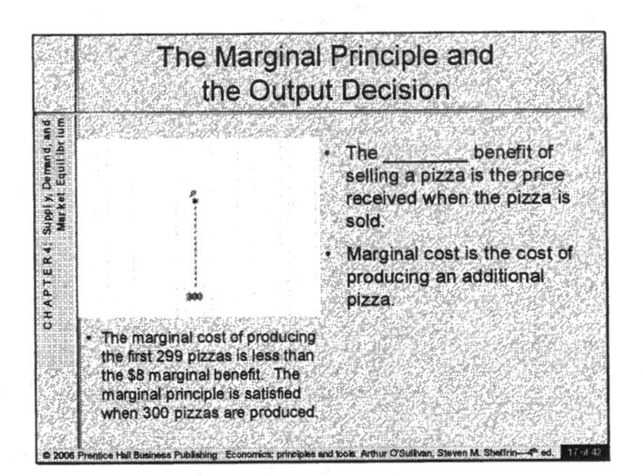
The Marginal Principle and the Output Decision
CHAPTER 4: Supply, Demand, and Market Equilibrium
300
The ______ benefit of selling a pizza is the price received when the pizza is sold.
Marginal cost is the cost of producing an additional pizza.
The marginal cost of producing the first 299 pizzas is less than the $8 marginal benefit. The marginal principle is satisfied when 300 pizzas are produced.
© 2006 Prentice Hall Business Publishing Economics: principles and tools Arthur O'Sullivan, Steven M. Sheffrin—4th ed.
17 of 42

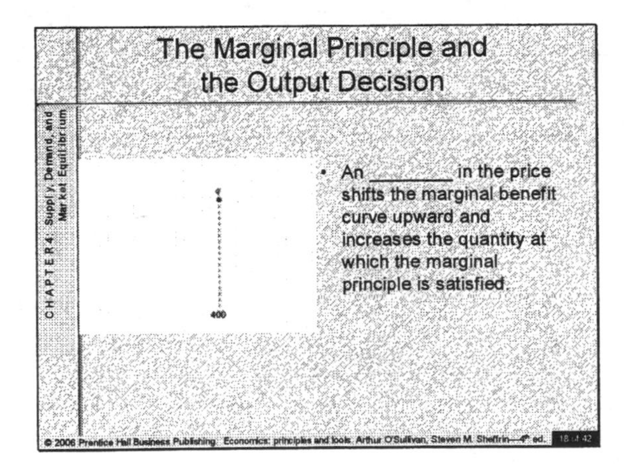
The Marginal Principle and the Output Decision
CHAPTER 4: Supply, Demand, and Market Equilibrium
400
An ______ in the price shifts the marginal benefit curve upward and increases the quantity at which the marginal principle is satisfied.
© 2006 Prentice Hall Business Publishing Economics: principles and tools Arthur O'Sullivan, Steven M. Sheffrin—4th ed.
18 of 42

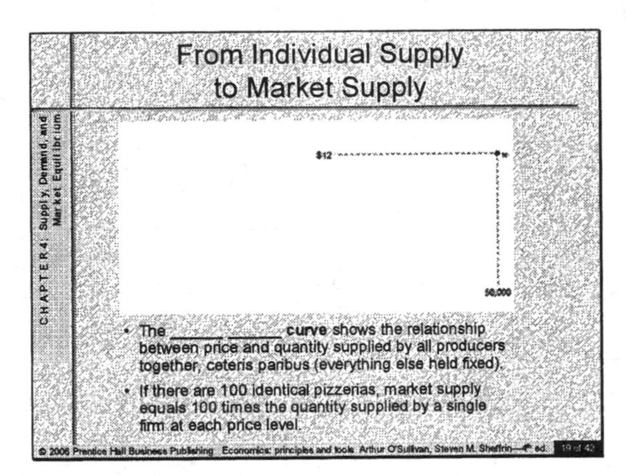
From Individual Supply
to Market Supply
CHAPTER 4: Supply, Demand, and Market Equilibrium
$12
50,000
• The ______ ______ curve shows the relationship between price and quantity supplied by all producers together, ceteris paribus (everything else held fixed).
• If there are 100 identical pizzerias, market supply equals 100 times the quantity supplied by a single firm at each price level.
© 2006 Prentice Hall Business Publishing Economics: principles and tools Arthur O'Sullivan, Steven M. Sheffrin—4th ed.
19 of 42

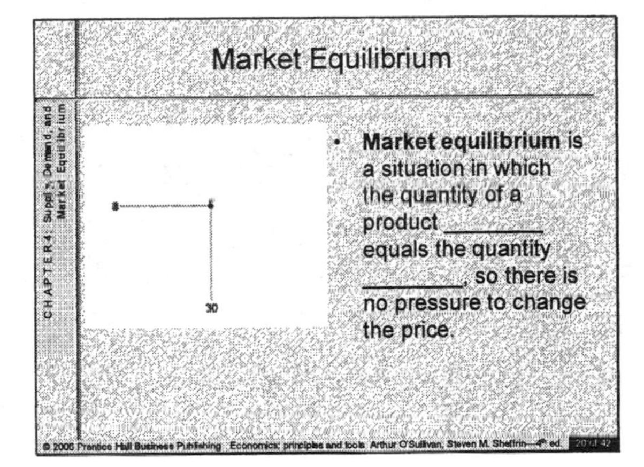
Market Equilibrium
CHAPTER 4: Supply, Demand, and Market Equilibrium
30
• Market equilibrium is a situation in which the quantity of a product ________ equals the quantity ________, so there is no pressure to change the price.
© 2006 Prentice Hall Business Publishing Economics: principles and tools Arthur O'Sullivan, Steven M. Sheffrin—4th ed.
20 of 42

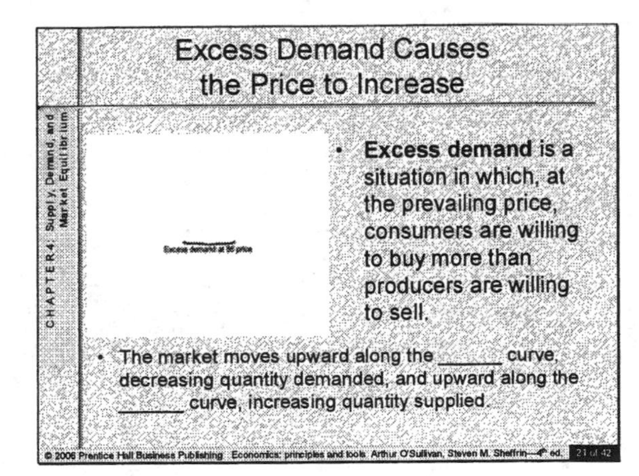
Excess Demand Causes
the Price to Increase
CHAPTER 4: Supply, Demand, and Market Equilibrium
• Excess demand is a situation in which, at the prevailing price, consumers are willing to buy more than producers are willing to sell.
• The market moves upward along the ______ curve, decreasing quantity demanded, and upward along the ______ curve, increasing quantity supplied.
© 2006 Prentice Hall Business Publishing Economics: principles and tools Arthur O'Sullivan, Steven M. Sheffrin—4th ed.
21 of 42

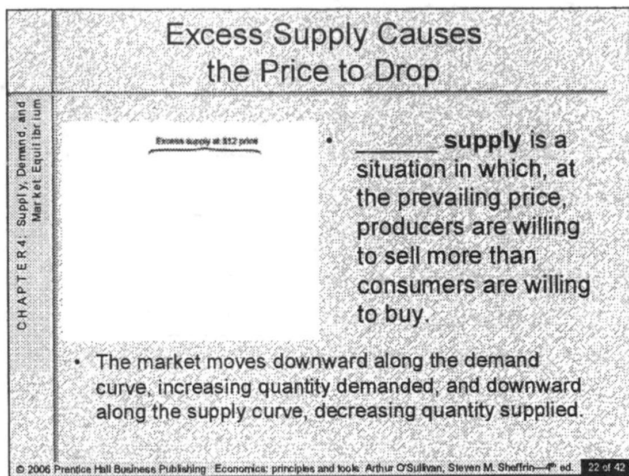
Excess Supply Causes the Price to Drop
CHAPTER 4: Supply, Demand, and Market Equilibrium
Excess supply at $12 price
• ______ supply is a situation in which, at the prevailing price, producers are willing to sell more than consumers are willing to buy.
• The market moves downward along the demand curve, increasing quantity demanded, and downward along the supply curve, decreasing quantity supplied.
© 2006 Prentice Hall Business Publishing Economics: principles and tools Arthur O'Sullivan, Steven M. Sheffrin—4th ed.
22 of 42

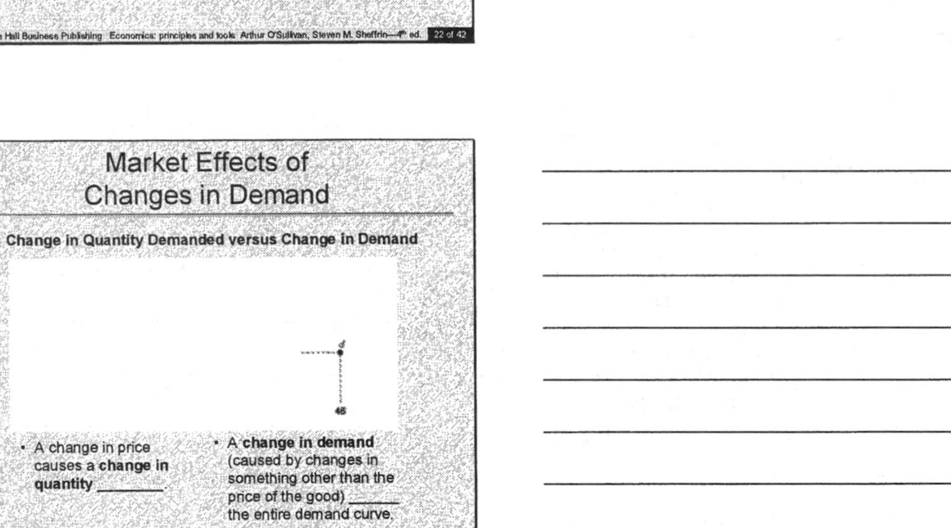
Market Effects of Changes in Demand
CHAPTER 4: Supply, Demand, and Market Equilibrium
Change in Quantity Demanded versus Change in Demand
46
• A change in price causes a change in quantity ______
• A change in demand (caused by changes in something other than the price of the good) ______ the entire demand curve.
© 2006 Prentice Hall Business Publishing Economics: principles and tools Arthur O'Sullivan, Steven M. Sheffrin—4th ed.
23 of 42

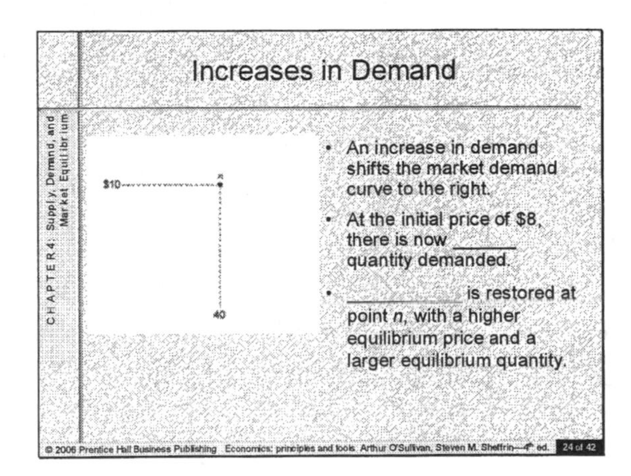
Increases in Demand
CHAPTER 4: Supply, Demand, and Market Equilibrium
$10
40
• An increase in demand shifts the market demand curve to the right.
• At the initial price of $8, there is now ______ quantity demanded.
• __________ is restored at point n, with a higher equilibrium price and a larger equilibrium quantity.
© 2006 Prentice Hall Business Publishing Economics: principles and tools Arthur O'Sullivan, Steven M. Sheffrin—4th ed.
24 of 42

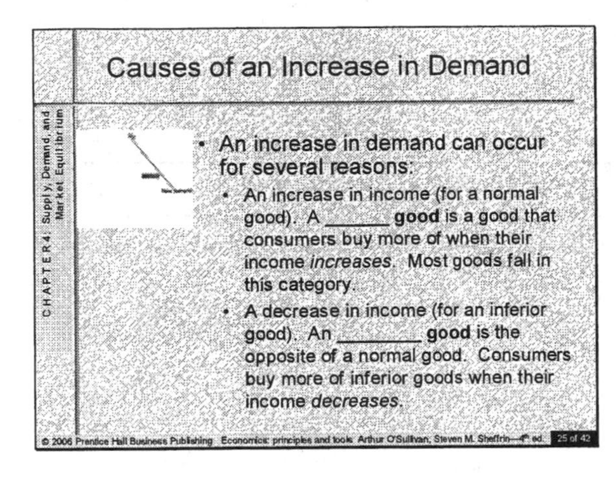
Causes of an Increase in Demand
CHAPTER 4: Supply, Demand, and Market Equilibrium
• An increase in demand can occur for several reasons:
• An increase in income (for a normal good). A ______ good is a good that consumers buy more of when their income increases. Most goods fall in this category.
• A decrease in income (for an inferior good). An ________ good is the opposite of a normal good. Consumers buy more of inferior goods when their income decreases.
© 2006 Prentice Hall Business Publishing Economics: principles and tools Arthur O'Sullivan, Steven M. Sheffrin—4th ed.
25 of 42

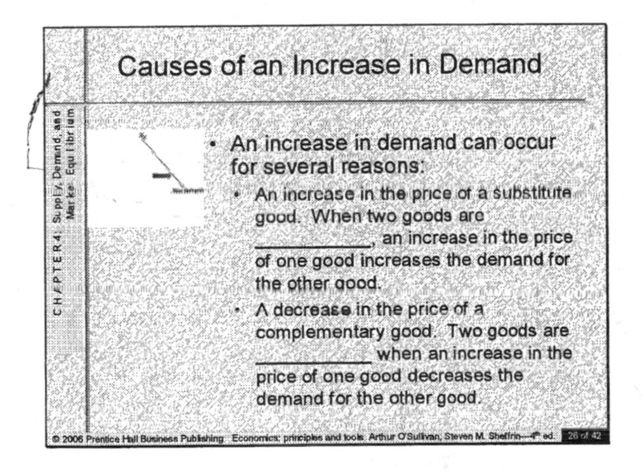
Causes of an Increase in Demand
CHAPTER 4: Supply, Demand, and Market Equilibrium
• An increase in demand can occur for several reasons:
• An increase in the price of a substitute good. When two goods are ___________, an increase in the price of one good increases the demand for the other good.
• A decrease in the price of a complementary good. Two goods are ___________ when an increase in the price of one good decreases the demand for the other good.
© 2006 Prentice Hall Business Publishing Economics: principles and tools Arthur O'Sullivan, Steven M. Sheffrin—4th ed.
26 of 42

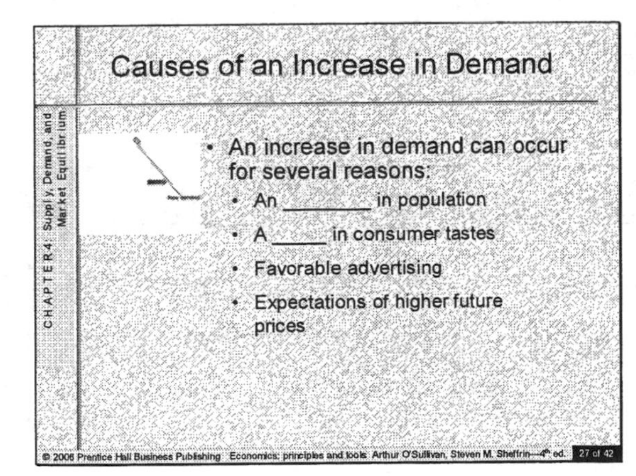
Causes of an Increase in Demand
CHAPTER 4: Supply, Demand, and Market Equilibrium
• An increase in demand can occur for several reasons:
• An ________ in population
• A _____ in consumer tastes
• Favorable advertising
• Expectations of higher future prices
© 2006 Prentice Hall Business Publishing Economics: principles and tools Arthur O'Sullivan, Steven M. Sheffrin—4th ed.
27 of 42

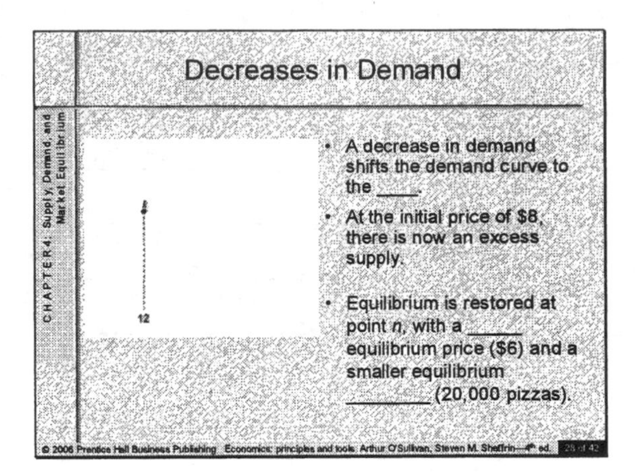

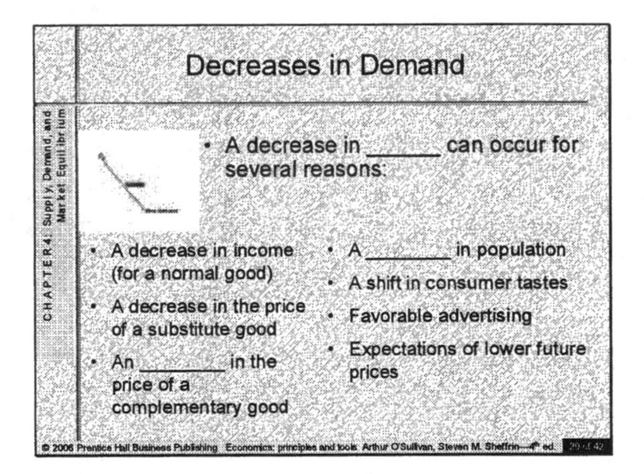

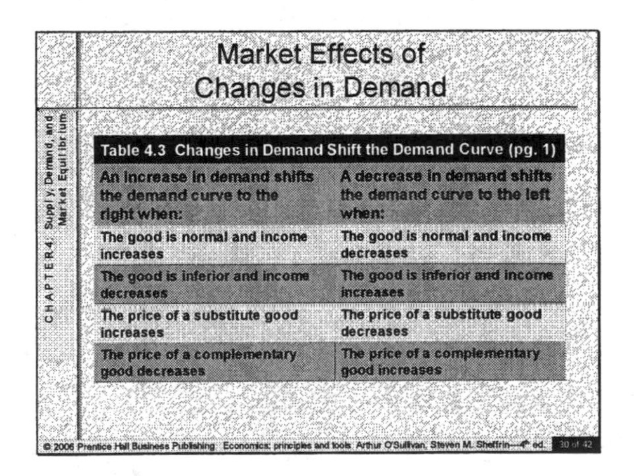

An increase in demand shifts the demand curve to the right when:	A decrease in demand shifts the demand curve to the left when:
The good is normal and income increases	The good is normal and income decreases
The good is inferior and income decreases	The good is inferior and income increases
The price of a substitute good increases	The price of a substitute good decreases
The price of a complementary good decreases	The price of a complementary good increases

Market Effects of Changes in Demand

CHAPTER 4: Supply, Demand, and Market Equilibrium

Table 4.3 Changes in Demand Shift the Demand Curve (pg. 2)

An increase in demand shifts the demand curve to the right when:	A decrease in demand shifts the demand curve to the left when:
Population increases	Population decreases
Consumer tastes shift in favor of the product	Consumer tastes shift away from the product
Consumers expect a higher price in the future	Consumers expect a lower price in the future

Market Effects of Changes in Supply

CHAPTER 4: Supply, Demand, and Market Equilibrium

Change in Quantity Supplied versus Change in Supply

36

- A change in price causes a **change in** ______ ______
- A **change in** ______ (caused by changes in something other than the price of the good) shifts the entire supply curve.

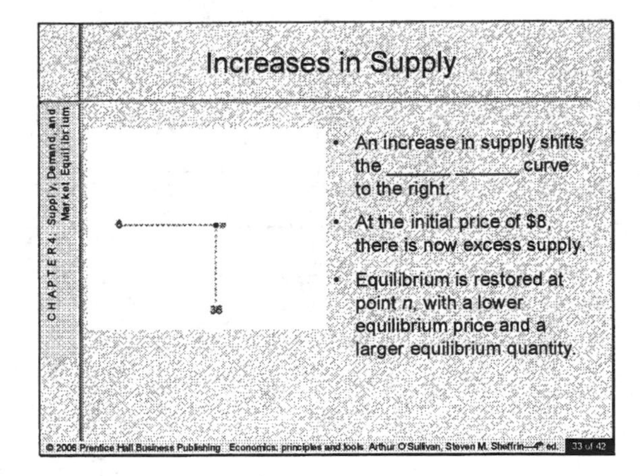

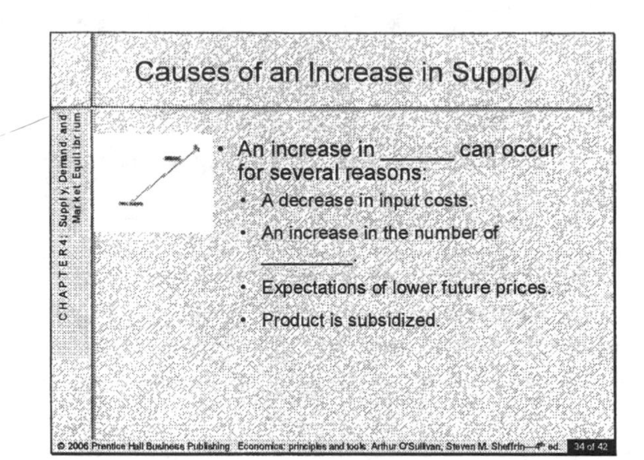
Causes of an Increase in Supply
CHAPTER 4: Supply, Demand, and Market Equilibrium
• An increase in ______ can occur for several reasons:
• A decrease in input costs.
• An increase in the number of ________.
• Expectations of lower future prices.
• Product is subsidized.
© 2006 Prentice Hall Business Publishing Economics: principles and tools Arthur O'Sullivan, Steven M. Sheffrin—4th ed. 34 of 42

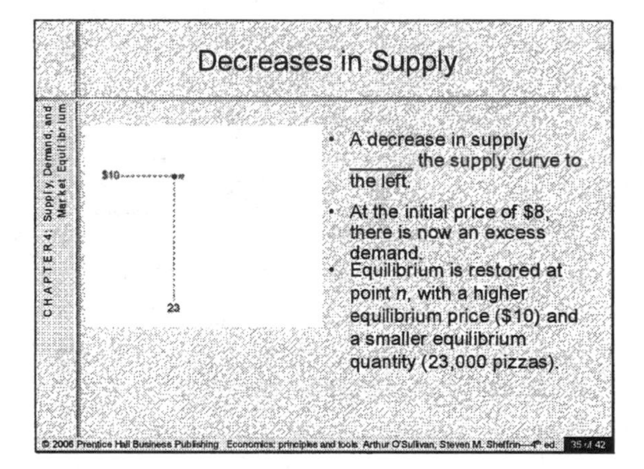
Decreases in Supply
CHAPTER 4: Supply, Demand, and Market Equilibrium
$10
23
• A decrease in supply ______ the supply curve to the left.
• At the initial price of $8, there is now an excess demand.
• Equilibrium is restored at point n, with a higher equilibrium price ($10) and a smaller equilibrium quantity (23,000 pizzas).
© 2006 Prentice Hall Business Publishing Economics: principles and tools Arthur O'Sullivan, Steven M. Sheffrin—4th ed. 35 of 42

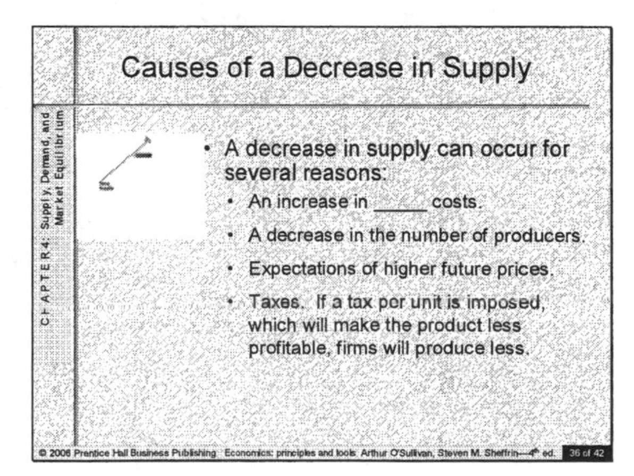
Causes of a Decrease in Supply
CHAPTER 4: Supply, Demand, and Market Equilibrium
• A decrease in supply can occur for several reasons:
• An increase in _____ costs.
• A decrease in the number of producers.
• Expectations of higher future prices.
• Taxes. If a tax per unit is imposed, which will make the product less profitable, firms will produce less.
© 2006 Prentice Hall Business Publishing Economics: principles and tools Arthur O'Sullivan, Steven M. Sheffrin—4th ed. 36 of 42

Market Effects of Changes in Supply

CHAPTER 4: Supply, Demand, and Market Equilibrium

Table 4.4 Changes in Supply Shift the Supply Curve

An increase in supply shifts the supply curve to the right when:	A decrease in supply shifts the supply curve to the left when:
The cost of an input decreases	The cost of an input increases
A technological advance decreases production cost	
The number of firms increases	The number of firms decreases
Producers expect a lower price in the future	Producers expect a higher price in the future
Product is subsidized	Product is taxed

© 2006 Prentice Hall Business Publishing Economics: principles and tools Arthur O'Sullivan, Steven M. Sheffrin—4th ed. 37 of 42

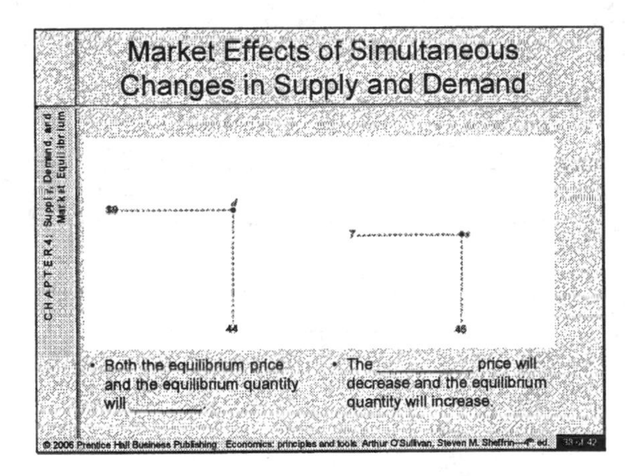

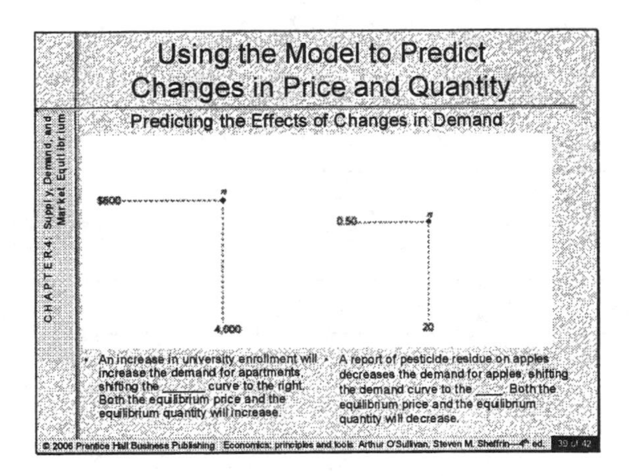

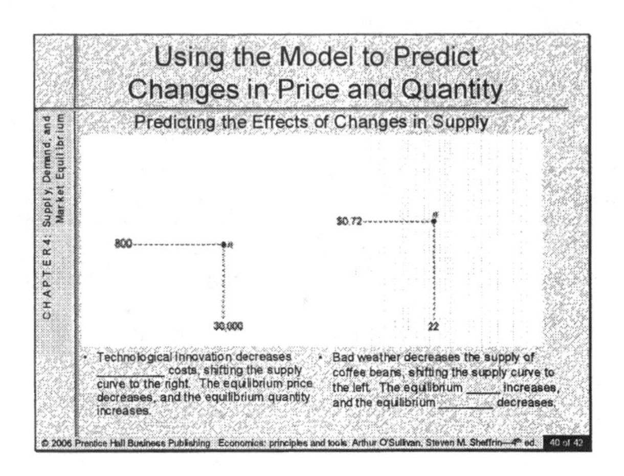

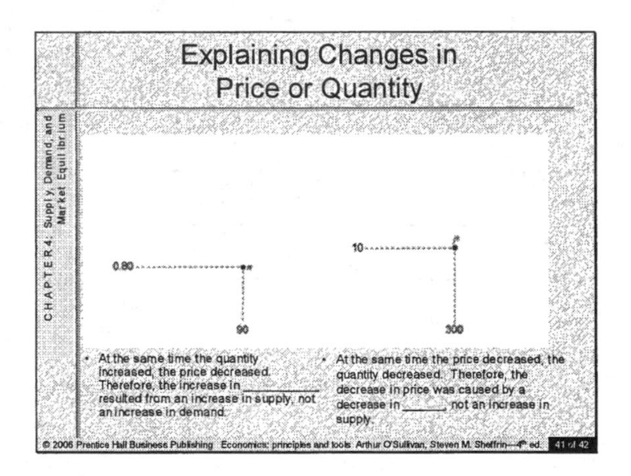

Key Terms

CHAPTER 4: Supply, Demand, and Market Equilibrium

- perfectly competitive market
- demand schedule
- individual demand curve
- quantity demanded
- law of demand
- change in quantity demanded
- substitution effect
- income effect
- market demand curve
- supply schedule
- quantity supplied
- change in quantity supplied
- market supply curve
- market equilibrium
- excess demand
- excess supply
- change in demand
- normal good
- substitute good
- complementary good
- inferior good
- change in supply

© 2006 Prentice Hall Business Publishing Economics: principles and tools Arthur O'Sullivan, Steven M. Sheffrin—4th ed.

Macroeconomics

CHAPTER 5: Measuring A Nation's Production and Income

- **Macroeconomics** is the branch of economics that deals with a nation's economy ___ ___ _____.
- Macroeconomics focuses on the economic issues—unemployment, inflation, growth, trade, and the gross domestic product—that are most often discussed in the media and in political ________.

© 2006 Prentice Hall Business Publishing Economics: principles and tools Arthur O'Sullivan, Steven M. Sheffrin—4th ed.

Macroeconomics

CHAPTER 5: Measuring A Nation's Production and Income

- Macroeconomics focuses on two basic issues:
  1. Long-run economic ______, or the factors behind the rise in living standards in modern economies.
  2. __________ in economic performance:
     - An economy is considered to be in a **recession** when it fails to grow for at least six consecutive months.
     - At other times, unemployment may not be a problem, but we become concerned about sustained increases in prices, or **inflation**.

© 2006 Prentice Hall Business Publishing Economics: principles and tools Arthur O'Sullivan, Steven M. Sheffrin—4th ed.

The "Flip" Sides of Macroeconomic Activity: Production and Income

CHAPTER 5: Measuring A Nation's Production and Income

- The terms "production" and "income" are the "____" sides of the macroeconomic "coin." Production leads to income and income leads to production.
- These two measures—a country's production and income—are ______ to a nation's economic health.

© 2006 Prentice Hall Business Publishing Economics: principles and tools Arthur O'Sullivan, Steven M. Sheffrin—4th ed.

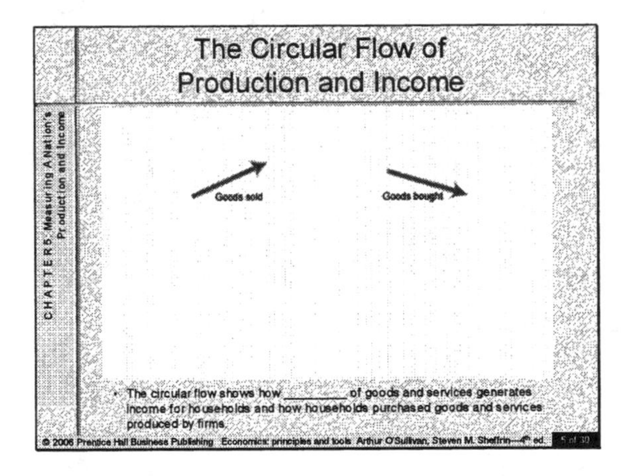

The Circular Flow of Production and Income

CHAPTER 5: Measuring A Nation's Production and Income

- In **factor, or ______ markets**, households supply labor to firms and also capital for land, buildings, machines, and equipment, used to produce output.
- **Product markets, or output markets,** are markets in which goods and services are sold to ________.

© 2006 Prentice Hall Business Publishing Economics: principles and tools Arthur O'Sullivan, Steven M. Sheffrin—4th ed.

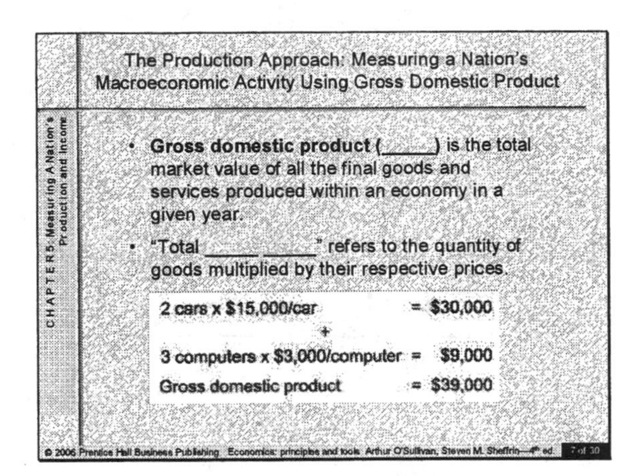

The Production Approach: Measuring a Nation's Macroeconomic Activity Using Gross Domestic Product

CHAPTER 5: Measuring A Nation's Production and Income

- An __________ **good** is a good that is used in the production process. It is not considered a final good or service.
- Only newly produced goods are included in GDP.

© 2006 Prentice Hall Business Publishing Economics: principles and tools Arthur O'Sullivan, Steven M. Sheffrin—4th ed. 8 of 30

The Production Approach: Measuring a Nation's Macroeconomic Activity Using Gross Domestic Product

CHAPTER 5: Measuring A Nation's Production and Income

Real-Nominal PRINCIPLE
What matters to people is the real value of money or income—its purchasing power—not the "face" value of money or income.

- _____ ____ is a measure of GDP that takes into account price changes. This measure of total output does not increase just because prices increase.
- When we use current prices to measure GDP, that is what we call ________ **GDP**, which can increase as a result of higher production or higher prices.

© 2006 Prentice Hall Business Publishing Economics: principles and tools Arthur O'Sullivan, Steven M. Sheffrin—4th ed. 9 of 30

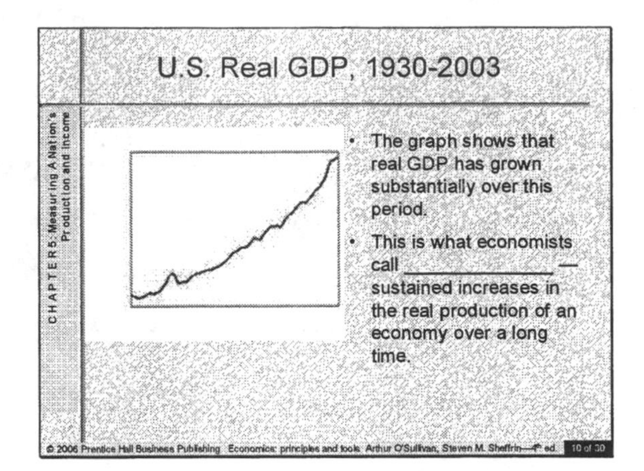

The Components of GDP

- Economists divide GDP into four broad __________ categories:
  1. Consumption expenditures: purchases by consumers.
  2. Private investment expenditures: purchases by firms.
  3. Government purchases: purchases by federal, state, and local governments.
  4. Net exports: net purchases by the foreign sector (domestic exports minus domestic imports).

Table 19.1 Composition of U.S. GDP, Third Quarter 2003 (billions of dollars expressed at annual rates)

GDP	Consumption Expenditures	Private Investment Expenditures	Government Purchases	Net Exports
11,107	7,836	1,689	2,072	-490

CHAPTER 5: Measuring A Nation's Production and Income

© 2006 Prentice Hall Business Publishing Economics: principles and tools Arthur O'Sullivan, Steven M. Sheffrin—4th ed.

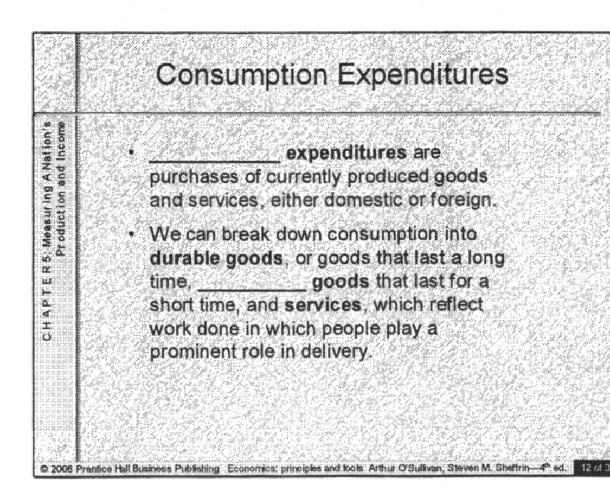

Private Investment Expenditures

- **Private __________ expenditures** include:
  1. Spending on new plants and equipment.
  2. Newly produced housing.
  3. Additions to inventories during the current year.

CHAPTER 5: Measuring A Nation's Production and Income

© 2006 Prentice Hall Business Publishing Economics: principles and tools Arthur O'Sullivan, Steven M. Sheffrin—4th ed. 13 of 30

Private Investment Expenditures

- New investment expenditures are called _______ **investment**.
- During the year, some of the existing plant, equipment, and housing will deteriorate. This wear and tear is called ___________.
- The true addition to the stock of capital of the economy is _____ **investment**. Net investment equals gross investment minus depreciation.

CHAPTER 5: Measuring A Nation's Production and Income

© 2006 Prentice Hall Business Publishing Economics: principles and tools Arthur O'Sullivan, Steven M. Sheffrin—4th ed. 14 of 30

Government Purchases

- **Government purchases** refer to purchases of newly produced goods and services by ___ _____ of government.
- _______ **payments** are funds paid to individuals but not associated with the production of goods and services.
- A large part of the federal government budget is not part of GDP.

CHAPTER 5: Measuring A Nation's Production and Income

© 2006 Prentice Hall Business Publishing Economics: principles and tools Arthur O'Sullivan, Steven M. Sheffrin—4th ed. 15 of 30

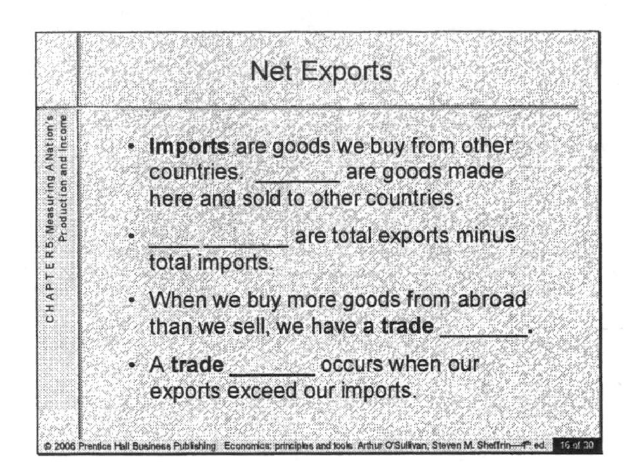
Net Exports
CHAPTER 5: Measuring A Nation's Production and Income
• Imports are goods we buy from other countries. _______ are goods made here and sold to other countries.
• ____ _______ are total exports minus total imports.
• When we buy more goods from abroad than we sell, we have a trade _______.
• A trade _______ occurs when our exports exceed our imports.
© 2006 Prentice Hall Business Publishing Economics: principles and tools Arthur O'Sullivan, Steven M. Sheffrin—4th ed.
16 of 30

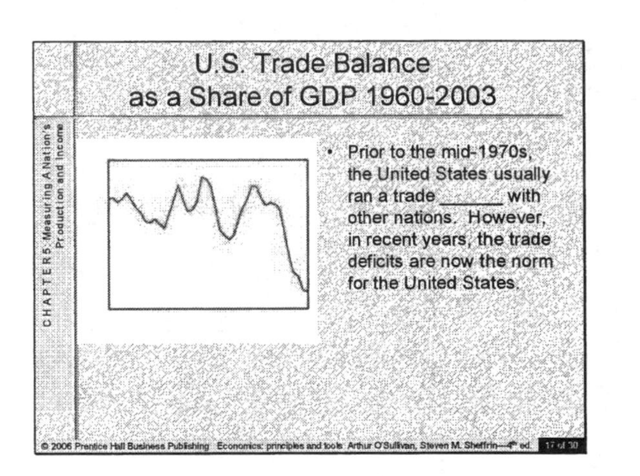
U.S. Trade Balance as a Share of GDP 1960-2003
CHAPTER 5: Measuring A Nation's Production and Income
• Prior to the mid-1970s, the United States usually ran a trade ______ with other nations. However, in recent years, the trade deficits are now the norm for the United States.
© 2006 Prentice Hall Business Publishing Economics: principles and tools Arthur O'Sullivan, Steven M. Sheffrin—4th ed.
17 of 30

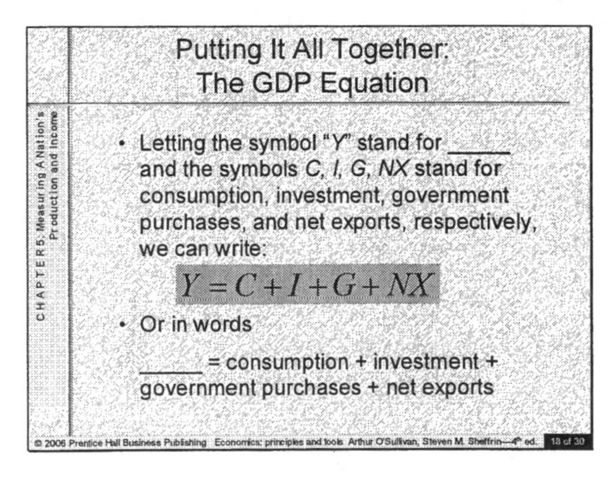
Putting It All Together: The GDP Equation
CHAPTER 5: Measuring A Nation's Production and Income
• Letting the symbol "Y" stand for _____ and the symbols C, I, G, NX stand for consumption, investment, government purchases, and net exports, respectively, we can write:
Y = C + I + G + NX
• Or in words
_____ = consumption + investment + government purchases + net exports
© 2006 Prentice Hall Business Publishing Economics: principles and tools Arthur O'Sullivan, Steven M. Sheffrin—4th ed.
18 of 30

The Income Approach: Measuring a Nation's Macroeconomic Activity Using National Income

CHAPTER 5: Measuring A Nation's Production and Income

- The income that _____ to the private sector is called **national income**. It is the income that all individuals and firms earn from their production.
- **Gross national product (____)** is the total income earned worldwide by U.S. firms and residents.
- When we subtract depreciation from GNP, we reach **net national product (____)**, where "net" means after depreciation.

© 2006 Prentice Hall Business Publishing Economics: principles and tools Arthur O'Sullivan, Steven M. Sheffrin—4th ed.

The Income Approach: Measuring a Nation's Macroeconomic Activity Using National Income

CHAPTER 5: Measuring A Nation's Production and Income

- The third and last adjustment we make to reach national income is to subtract _____ _____, which are sales taxes or excise taxes on products.

Table 19.2 From GDP to National Income, Third Quarter 2003 (billions of dollars)

Gross domestic product plus net income from abroad =	11,107
Gross national product minus depreciation =	11,144
Net national product minus indirect taxes (and other adjustments) =	9,836
National income	**9,782**

© 2006 Prentice Hall Business Publishing Economics: principles and tools Arthur O'Sullivan, Steven M. Sheffrin—4th ed.

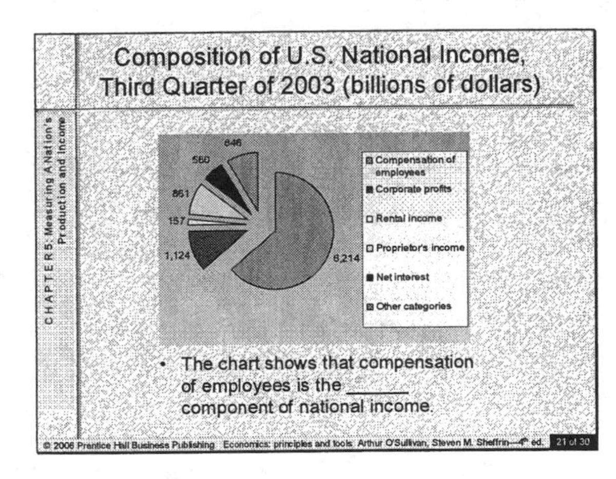

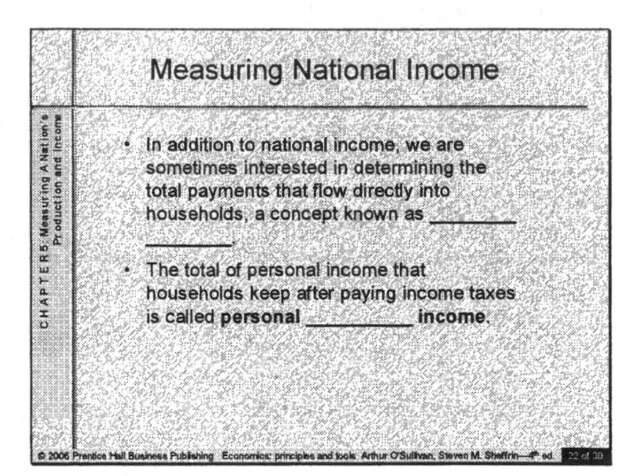
Measuring National Income
In addition to national income, we are sometimes interested in determining the total payments that flow directly into households, a concept known as ________ ________.
The total of personal income that households keep after paying income taxes is called personal ________ income.
CHAPTER 5: Measuring A Nation's Production and Income
© 2006 Prentice Hall Business Publishing Economics: principles and tools Arthur O'Sullivan, Steven M. Sheffrin—4th ed.

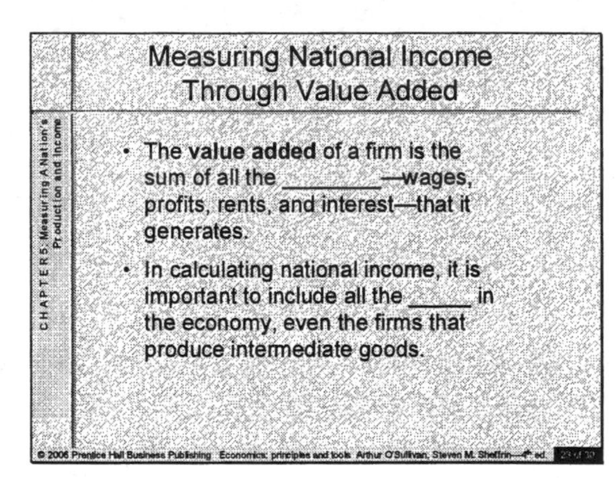
Measuring National Income Through Value Added
The value added of a firm is the sum of all the ________—wages, profits, rents, and interest—that it generates.
In calculating national income, it is important to include all the _____ in the economy, even the firms that produce intermediate goods.
CHAPTER 5: Measuring A Nation's Production and Income
© 2006 Prentice Hall Business Publishing Economics: principles and tools Arthur O'Sullivan, Steven M. Sheffrin—4th ed.

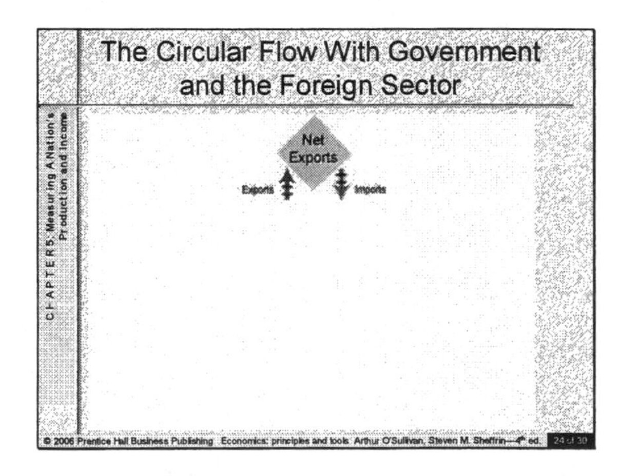
The Circular Flow With Government and the Foreign Sector
Net Exports
Exports
Imports
CHAPTER 5: Measuring A Nation's Production and Income
© 2006 Prentice Hall Business Publishing Economics: principles and tools Arthur O'Sullivan, Steven M. Sheffrin—4th ed.

Measuring Real Versus Nominal GDP

CHAPTER 5: Measuring A Nation's Production and Income

Table 19.3 GDP Data for a Simple Economy

	Quantity Produced		Price		
Year	Cars	Computers	Cars	Computers	Nominal GDP
2006	4	1	$10,000	$5,000	$45,000
2007	5	3	$12,000	$5,000	$75,000

- To calculate real GDP we use constant prices.

	Quantity Produced		Price		
Year	Cars	Computers	Cars	Computers	Real GDP
2006	4	1	$10,000	$5,000	$45,000
2007	5	3	**$10,000**	**$5,000**	$65,000

Growth of real GDP: **($65,000 - $45,000)/$45,000 = .444 or 44.4%**

© 2006 Prentice Hall Business Publishing Economics: principles and tools Arthur O'Sullivan, Steven M. Sheffrin—4th ed. 25 of 30

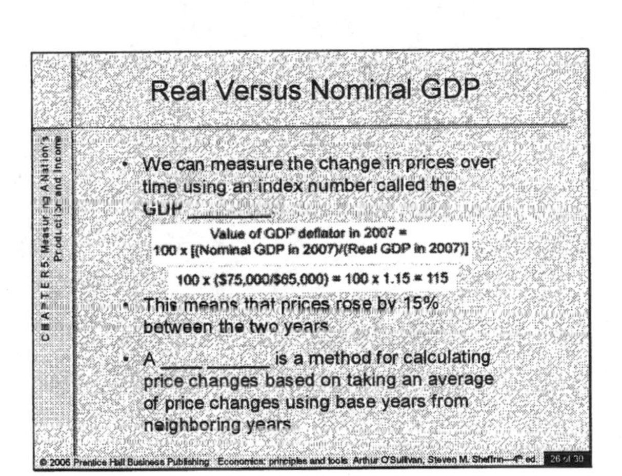

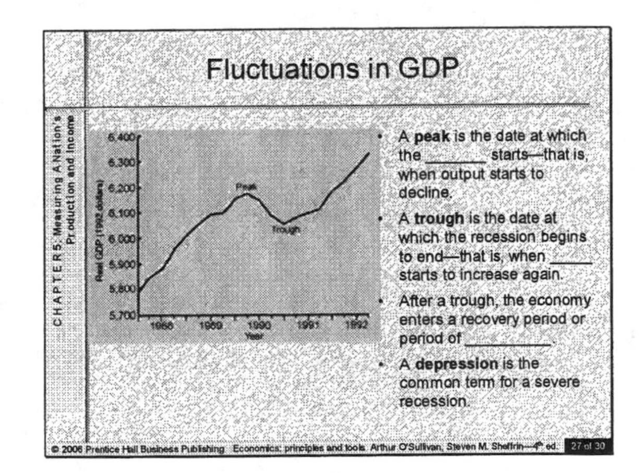

Fluctuations in GDP

CHAPTER 5: Measuring A Nation's Production and Income

Table 19.4 Ten Postwar Recessions

Peak	Trough	Percent Decline in Real GDP
November 1948	October 1949	-1.5
July 1953	May 1954	-3.2
August 1957	April 1958	-3.3
April 1960	February 1961	-1.2
December 1969	November 1970	-1.0
November 1973	March 1975	-4.9
January 1980	July 1980	-2.5
July 1981	November 1982	-3.0
July 1990	March 1991	-1.4
March 2001	November 2001	-0.6

© 2006 Prentice Hall Business Publishing Economics: principles and tools Arthur O'Sullivan, Steven M. Sheffrin—4th ed. 28 of 30

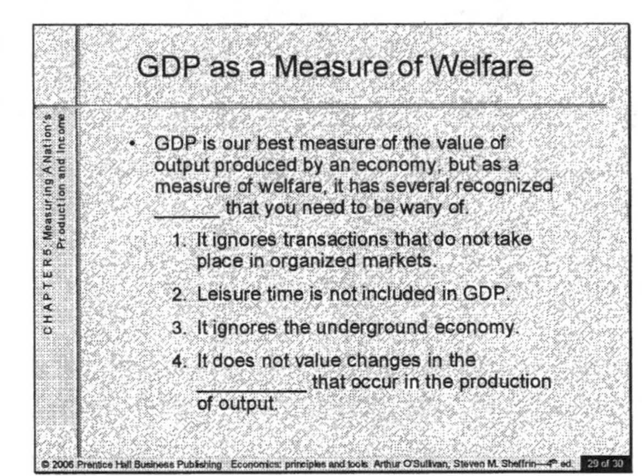

GDP as a Measure of Welfare

CHAPTER 5: Measuring A Nation's Production and Income

- GDP is our best measure of the value of output produced by an economy, but as a measure of welfare, it has several recognized ______ that you need to be wary of.
  1. It ignores transactions that do not take place in organized markets.
  2. Leisure time is not included in GDP.
  3. It ignores the underground economy.
  4. It does not value changes in the __________ that occur in the production of output.

© 2006 Prentice Hall Business Publishing Economics: principles and tools Arthur O'Sullivan, Steven M. Sheffrin—4th ed. 29 of 30

Key Terms

CHAPTER 5: Measuring A Nation's Production and Income

chain index
consumption expenditures
depreciation
depression
durable goods
economic growth
expansion
GDP deflator
government purchases
gross domestic product (GDP)
gross investment
gross national product (GNP)
indirect taxes
intermediate goods
macroeconomics
national income
net exports
net investment
net national product (NNP)
nominal GDP
nondurable goods
peak
personal income
personal disposable income
private investment expenditures
real GDP
recession
services
trade deficit
trade surplus
transfer payments
trough
value added

© 2006 Prentice Hall Business Publishing Economics: principles and tools Arthur O'Sullivan, Steven M. Sheffrin—4th ed. 30 of 30

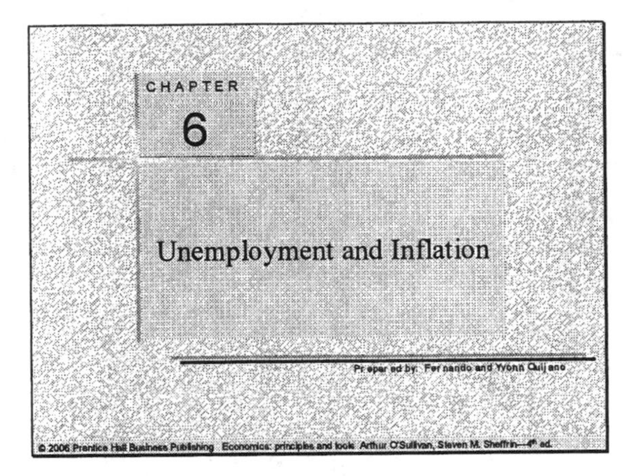

Examining Unemployment

- During periods of poor economic performance, such as economic _________ when real GDP declines, unemployment rises sharply and becomes a cause of public concern.
- During times of good economic performance and rapid economic growth, ____________ is reduced but does not disappear.

CHAPTER 6: Unemployment and Inflation

© 2006 Prentice Hall Business Publishing Economics: principles and tools Arthur O'Sullivan, Steven M. Sheffrin—4th ed. 2 of 28

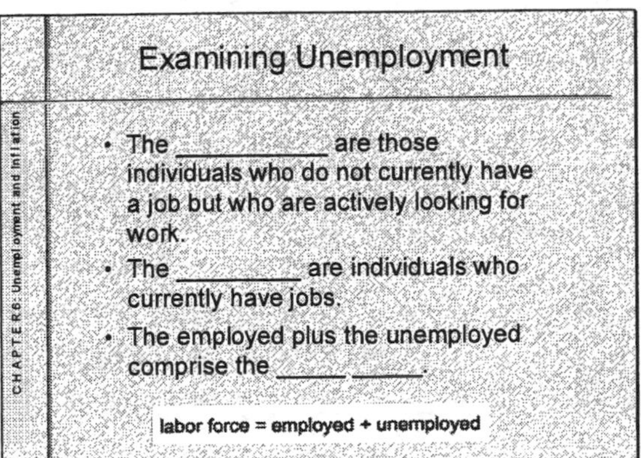

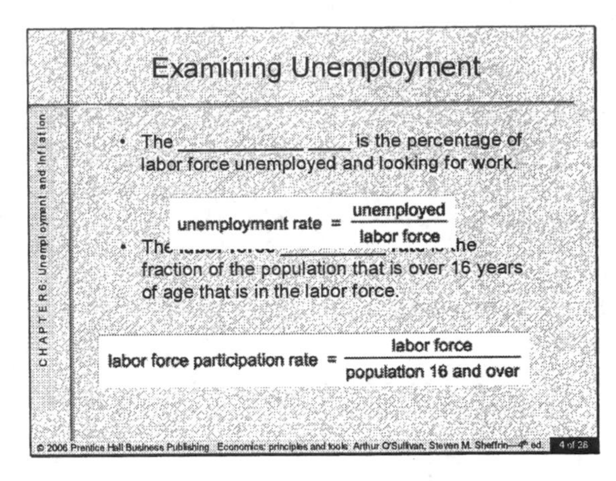
Examining Unemployment
The __________ ____ is the percentage of labor force unemployed and looking for work.
unemployment rate = unemployed / labor force
The labor force ______ rate is the fraction of the population that is over 16 years of age that is in the labor force.
labor force participation rate = labor force / population 16 and over
CHAPTER 6: Unemployment and Inflation
© 2006 Prentice Hall Business Publishing Economics: principles and tools Arthur O'Sullivan, Steven M. Sheffrin—4th ed.
4 of 28

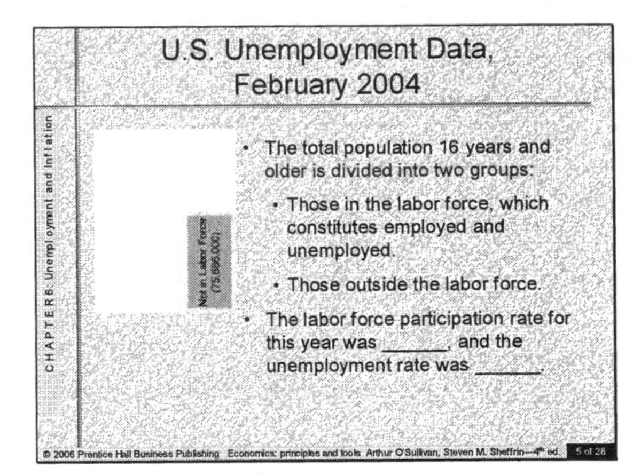
U.S. Unemployment Data, February 2004
Not in Labor Force (75,666,000)
The total population 16 years and older is divided into two groups:
Those in the labor force, which constitutes employed and unemployed.
Those outside the labor force.
The labor force participation rate for this year was ______, and the unemployment rate was ______.
CHAPTER 6: Unemployment and Inflation
© 2006 Prentice Hall Business Publishing Economics: principles and tools Arthur O'Sullivan, Steven M. Sheffrin—4th ed.
5 of 28

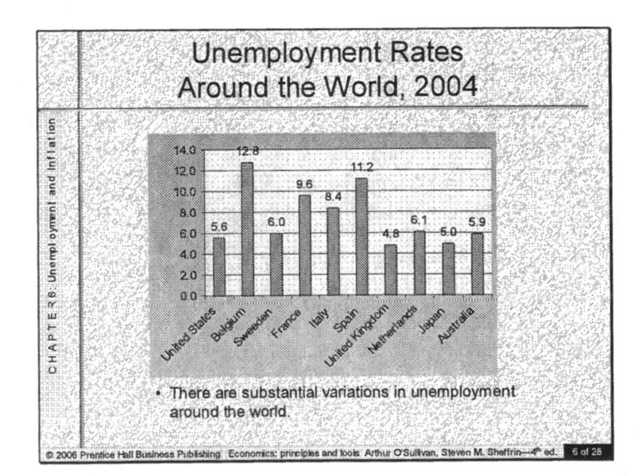
Unemployment Rates Around the World, 2004
14.0
12.0
10.0
8.0
6.0
4.0
2.0
0.0
5.6
12.8
6.0
9.6
8.4
11.2
4.8
6.1
5.0
5.9
United States
Belgium
Sweeden
France
Italy
Spain
United Kingdom
Netherlands
Japan
Australia
There are substantial variations in unemployment around the world.
CHAPTER 6: Unemployment and Inflation
© 2006 Prentice Hall Business Publishing Economics: principles and tools Arthur O'Sullivan, Steven M. Sheffrin—4th ed.
6 of 28

Alternative Measures of Unemployment and Why They're Important

CHAPTER 6: Unemployment and Inflation

- The official statistics for unemployment do not include the full range of individuals who would like to participate fully in the labor market.
  - Individuals who want to work, have searched for work in the prior year, but are not currently looking for work because they believe they won't be able to find a job are called __________ **workers**.
  - Individuals who would like to work, have searched for work in the recent past, but have stopped looking for work for a variety of reasons are known as __________ __________ **workers**.
  - Workers who would like to be employed full-time but hold part-time jobs are known as **individuals working** ____ ____ **for economic reasons**.

© 2006 Prentice Hall Business Publishing Economics: principles and tools Arthur O'Sullivan, Steven M. Sheffrin—4th ed. 7 of 28

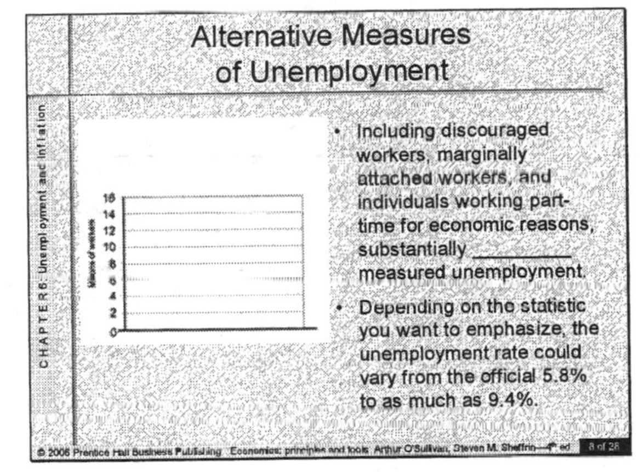

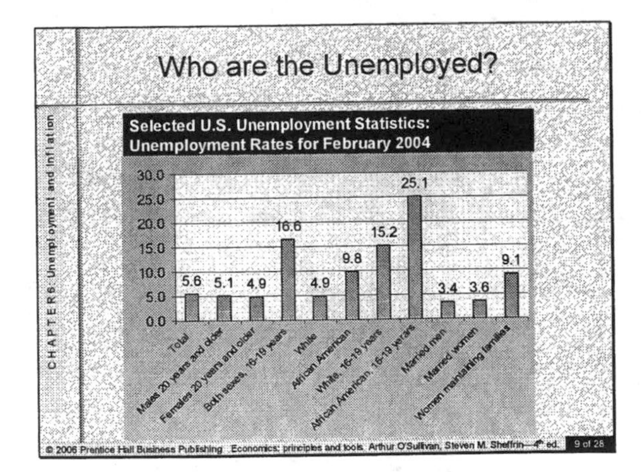

Who Are the Unemployed?

CHAPTER 6: Unemployment and Inflation

- Different groups of people suffer more unemployment than other groups.
- Unemployment rates vary somewhat as GDP rises and falls.
- Unemployment due to recurring calendar effects is called ______________________.

© 2006 Prentice Hall Business Publishing Economics: principles and tools Arthur O'Sullivan, Steven M. Sheffrin—4th ed. 10 of 28

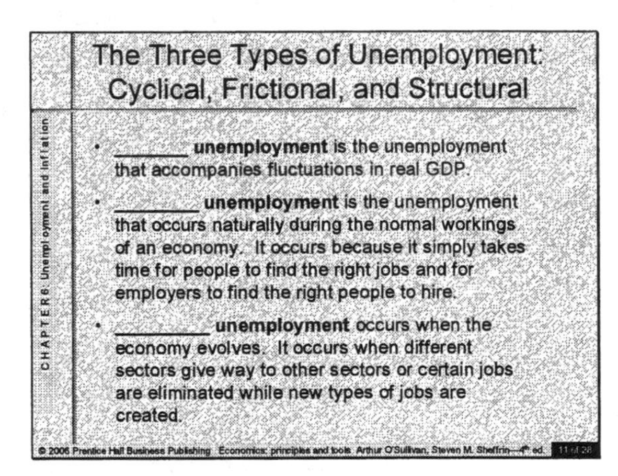

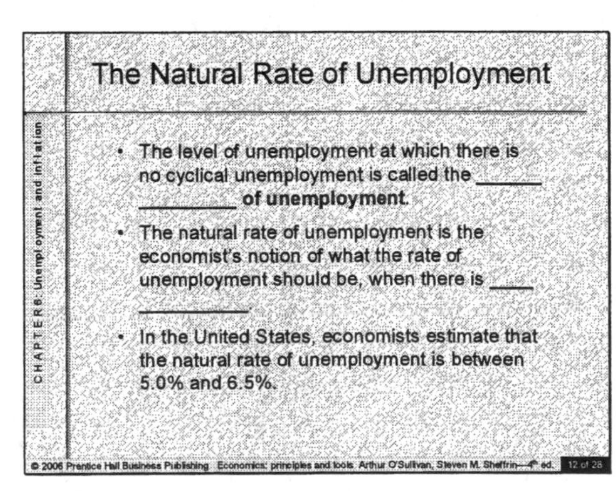

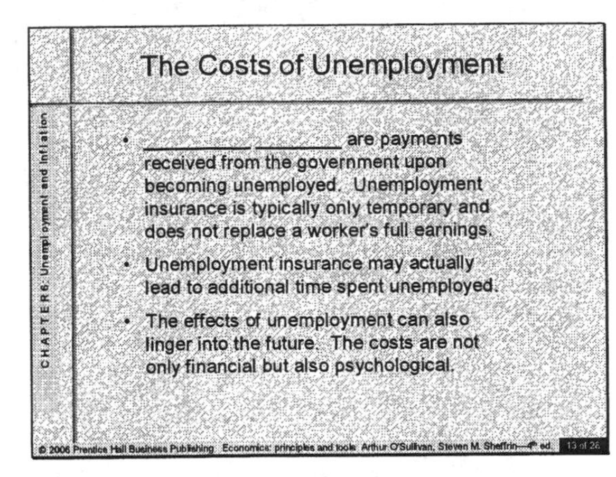
The Costs of Unemployment
CHAPTER 6: Unemployment and Inflation
• __________ ________ are payments received from the government upon becoming unemployed. Unemployment insurance is typically only temporary and does not replace a worker's full earnings.
• Unemployment insurance may actually lead to additional time spent unemployed.
• The effects of unemployment can also linger into the future. The costs are not only financial but also psychological.
© 2006 Prentice Hall Business Publishing Economics: principles and tools Arthur O'Sullivan, Steven M. Sheffrin—4th ed.
13 of 26

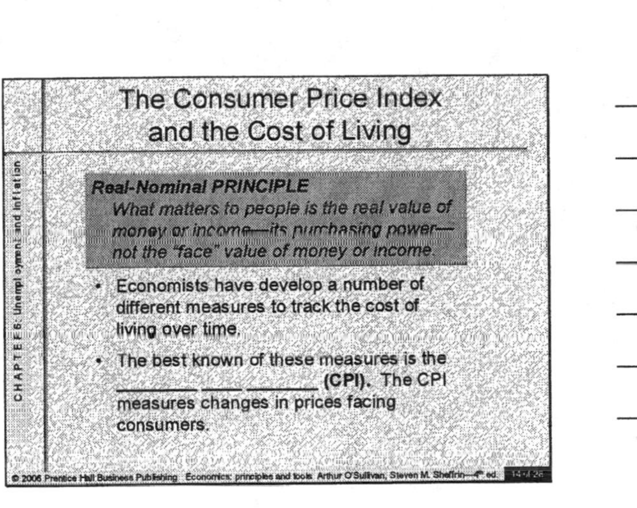
The Consumer Price Index and the Cost of Living
CHAPTER 6: Unemployment and Inflation
Real-Nominal PRINCIPLE
What matters to people is the real value of money or income—its purchasing power—not the "face" value of money or income.
• Economists have develop a number of different measures to track the cost of living over time.
• The best known of these measures is the ________ ____ ______ (CPI). The CPI measures changes in prices facing consumers.
© 2006 Prentice Hall Business Publishing Economics: principles and tools Arthur O'Sullivan, Steven M. Sheffrin—4th ed.
14 of 26

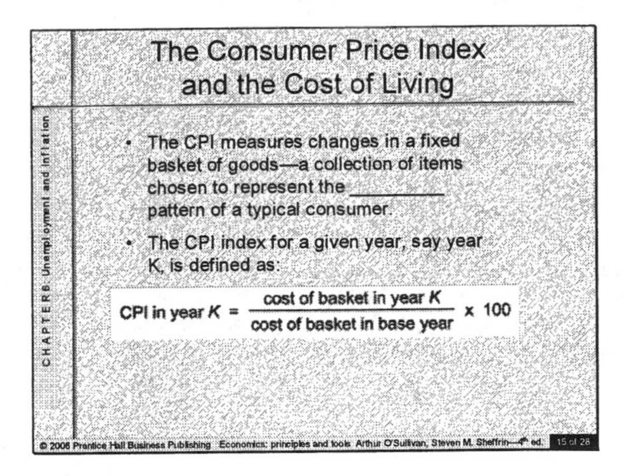
The Consumer Price Index and the Cost of Living
CHAPTER 6: Unemployment and Inflation
• The CPI measures changes in a fixed basket of goods—a collection of items chosen to represent the ________ pattern of a typical consumer.
• The CPI index for a given year, say year K, is defined as:
CPI in year K = cost of basket in year K / cost of basket in base year x 100
© 2006 Prentice Hall Business Publishing Economics: principles and tools Arthur O'Sullivan, Steven M. Sheffrin—4th ed.
15 of 26

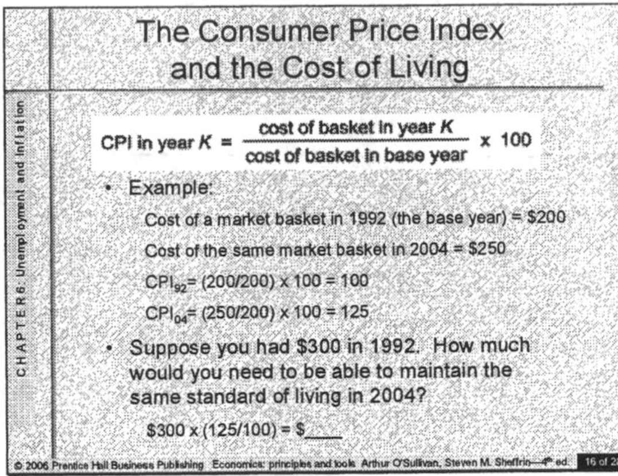

The Consumer Price Index and the Cost of Living
CPI in year K = cost of basket in year K / cost of basket in base year x 100
• Example:
Cost of a market basket in 1992 (the base year) = $200
Cost of the same market basket in 2004 = $250
CPI92= (200/200) x 100 = 100
CPI04= (250/200) x 100 = 125
• Suppose you had $300 in 1992. How much would you need to be able to maintain the same standard of living in 2004?
$300 x (125/100) = $____
CHAPTER 6: Unemployment and Inflation
© 2006 Prentice Hall Business Publishing Economics: principles and tools Arthur O'Sullivan, Steven M. Sheffrin—4th ed.
16 of 28

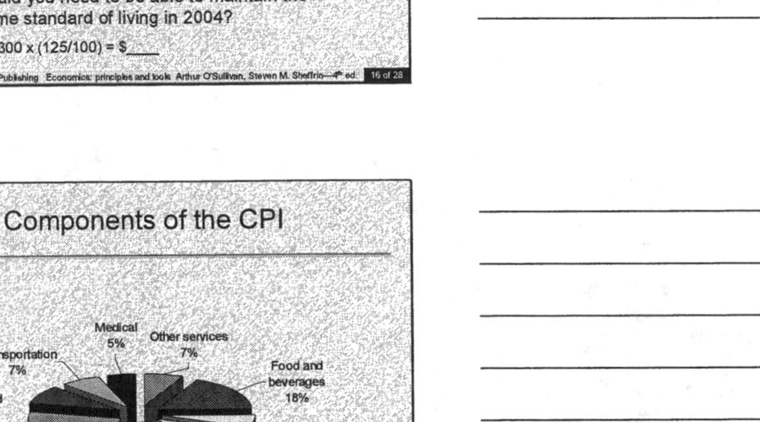

Components of the CPI
Medical 5%
Other services 7%
Transportation 7%
Food and beverages 18%
Household services 9%
Apparel 6%
Rent 26%
Nondurables 11%
Durables 11%
CHAPTER 6: Unemployment and Inflation
© 2006 Prentice Hall Business Publishing Economics: principles and tools Arthur O'Sullivan, Steven M. Sheffrin—4th ed.
17 of 28

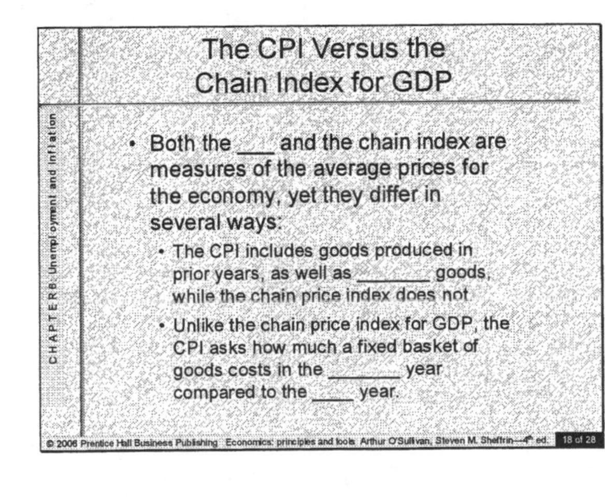

The CPI Versus the Chain Index for GDP
• Both the ___ and the chain index are measures of the average prices for the economy, yet they differ in several ways:
• The CPI includes goods produced in prior years, as well as _______ goods, while the chain price index does not.
• Unlike the chain price index for GDP, the CPI asks how much a fixed basket of goods costs in the _______ year compared to the ____ year.
CHAPTER 6: Unemployment and Inflation
© 2006 Prentice Hall Business Publishing Economics: principles and tools Arthur O'Sullivan, Steven M. Sheffrin—4th ed.
18 of 28

Problems in Measuring Changes in Prices

CHAPTER 6: Unemployment and Inflation

- In reality, all indexes tend to _______ actual price changes, primarily because we have a difficult time measuring quality improvements.
- Economists believe that we overestimate the inflation rate by between 0.5% and 1.5% each year.
- Government programs, such as social security, automatically _______ payments based on changes in the CPI and this increase tends to be larger than it should be.

© 2006 Prentice Hall Business Publishing Economics: principles and tools Arthur O'Sullivan, Steven M. Sheffrin—4th ed.

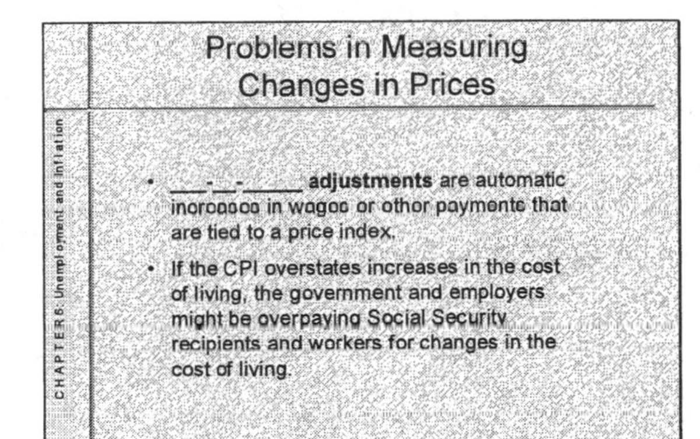

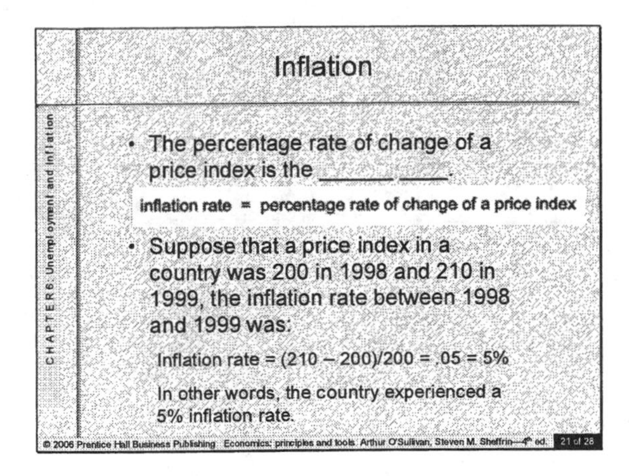

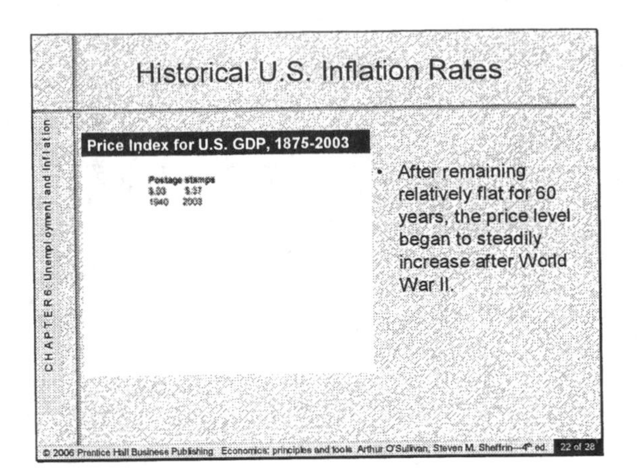

Historical U.S. Inflation Rates

Table 20.1 Prices of Selected Goods, 1940	
Gallon of gasoline	$0.18
Loaf of bread	0.08
Gallon of milk	0.34
Postage stamps	0.03
House	$6,550
Car	$800
Haircut in New York City	0.50
Movie tickets in New York City	0.25
Men's tweed sports jacket in New York City	$15
Snake tattoo on arm	0.25

CHAPTER 6: Unemployment and Inflation

© 2006 Prentice Hall Business Publishing Economics: principles and tools Arthur O'Sullivan, Steven M. Sheffrin—4th ed. 23 of 28

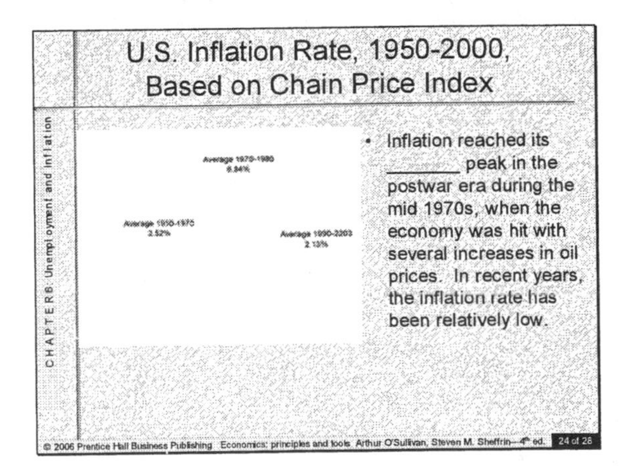

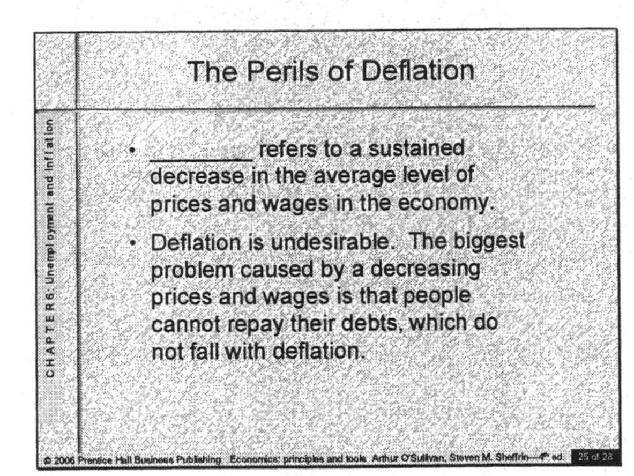
The Perils of Deflation
CHAPTER 6: Unemployment and Inflation
• ________ refers to a sustained decrease in the average level of prices and wages in the economy.
• Deflation is undesirable. The biggest problem caused by a decreasing prices and wages is that people cannot repay their debts, which do not fall with deflation.
© 2006 Prentice Hall Business Publishing Economics: principles and tools Arthur O'Sullivan, Steven M. Sheffrin—4th ed.
25 of 28

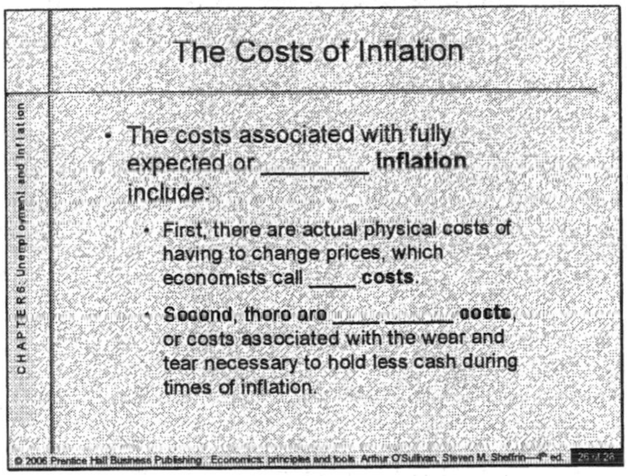
The Costs of Inflation
CHAPTER 6: Unemployment and Inflation
• The costs associated with fully expected or ________ inflation include:
• First, there are actual physical costs of having to change prices, which economists call ____ costs.
• Second, there are ____ ______ costs, or costs associated with the wear and tear necessary to hold less cash during times of inflation.
© 2006 Prentice Hall Business Publishing Economics: principles and tools Arthur O'Sullivan, Steven M. Sheffrin—4th ed.
26 of 28

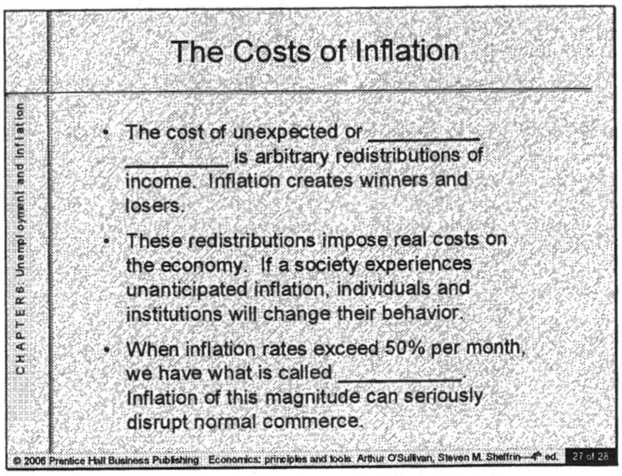
The Costs of Inflation
CHAPTER 6: Unemployment and Inflation
• The cost of unexpected or ________ ________ is arbitrary redistributions of income. Inflation creates winners and losers.
• These redistributions impose real costs on the economy. If a society experiences unanticipated inflation, individuals and institutions will change their behavior.
• When inflation rates exceed 50% per month, we have what is called __________. Inflation of this magnitude can seriously disrupt normal commerce.
© 2006 Prentice Hall Business Publishing Economics: principles and tools Arthur O'Sullivan, Steven M. Sheffrin—4th ed.
27 of 28

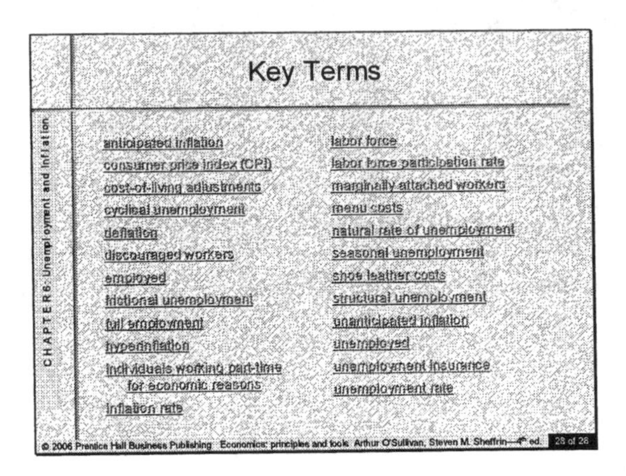
Key Terms
CHAPTER 6: Unemployment and Inflation
anticipated inflation
consumer price index (CPI)
cost-of-living adjustments
cyclical unemployment
deflation
discouraged workers
employed
frictional unemployment
full employment
hyperinflation
individuals working part-time for economic reasons
inflation rate
labor force
labor force participation rate
marginally attached workers
menu costs
natural rate of unemployment
seasonal unemployment
shoe leather costs
structural unemployment
unanticipated inflation
unemployed
unemployment insurance
unemployment rate
© 2006 Prentice Hall Business Publishing Economics: principles and tools Arthur O'Sullivan, Steven M. Sheffrin—4th ed.
28 of 28

CHAPTER
7
The Economy
at Full Employment
Prepared by: Fernando and Yvonn Quijano
© 2006 Prentice Hall Business Publishing Economics: principles and tools Arthur O'Sullivan, Steven M. Sheffrin—4th ed.

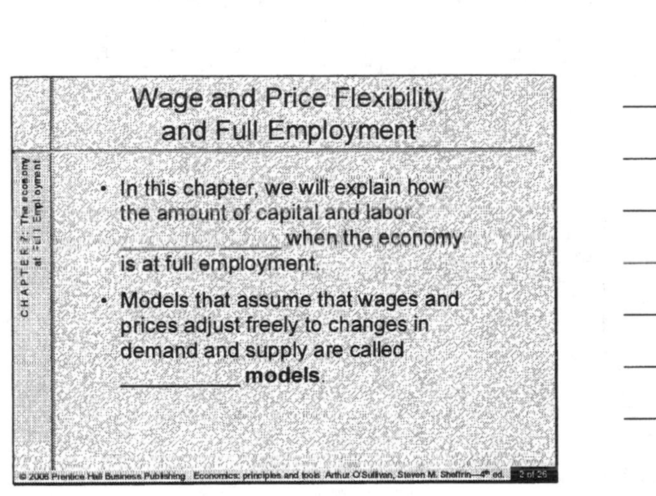
Wage and Price Flexibility
and Full Employment
CHAPTER 7: The economy at Full Employment
• In this chapter, we will explain how the amount of capital and labor ________ _____ when the economy is at full employment.
• Models that assume that wages and prices adjust freely to changes in demand and supply are called _________ models.
© 2006 Prentice Hall Business Publishing Economics: principles and tools Arthur O'Sullivan, Steven M. Sheffrin—4th ed.
2 of 26

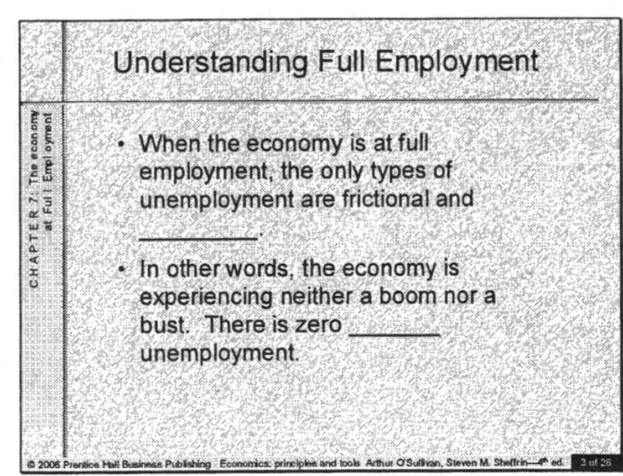
Understanding Full Employment
CHAPTER 7: The economy at Full Employment
• When the economy is at full employment, the only types of unemployment are frictional and _________.
• In other words, the economy is experiencing neither a boom nor a bust. There is zero _______ unemployment.
© 2006 Prentice Hall Business Publishing Economics: principles and tools Arthur O'Sullivan, Steven M. Sheffrin—4th ed.
3 of 26

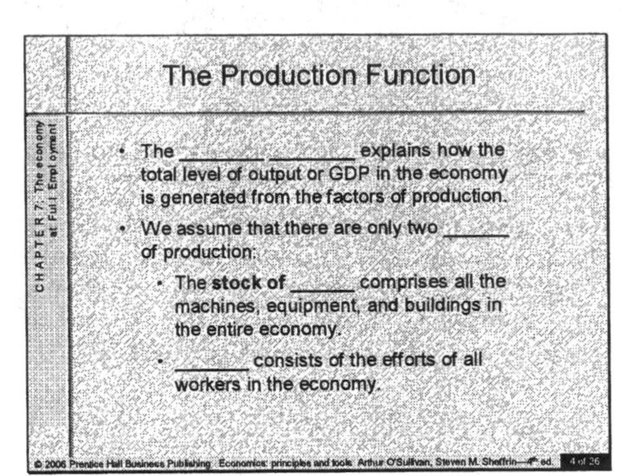
The Production Function
CHAPTER 7: The economy at Full Employment
• The ________ ________ explains how the total level of output or GDP in the economy is generated from the factors of production.
• We assume that there are only two ______ of production:
• The **stock of** ______ comprises all the machines, equipment, and buildings in the entire economy.
• ______ consists of the efforts of all workers in the economy.
© 2006 Prentice Hall Business Publishing Economics: principles and tools Arthur O'Sullivan, Steven M. Sheffrin—4th ed.
4 of 26

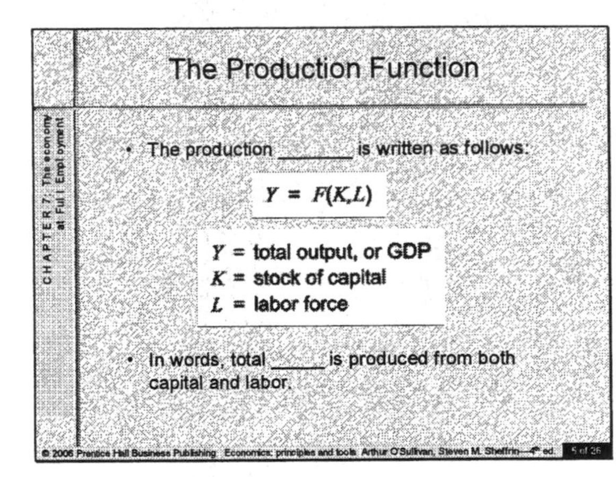
The Production Function
CHAPTER 7: The economy at Full Employment
• The production ______ is written as follows:
Y = F(K,L)
Y = total output, or GDP
K = stock of capital
L = labor force
• In words, total _____ is produced from both capital and labor.
© 2006 Prentice Hall Business Publishing Economics: principles and tools Arthur O'Sullivan, Steven M. Sheffrin—4th ed.
5 of 26

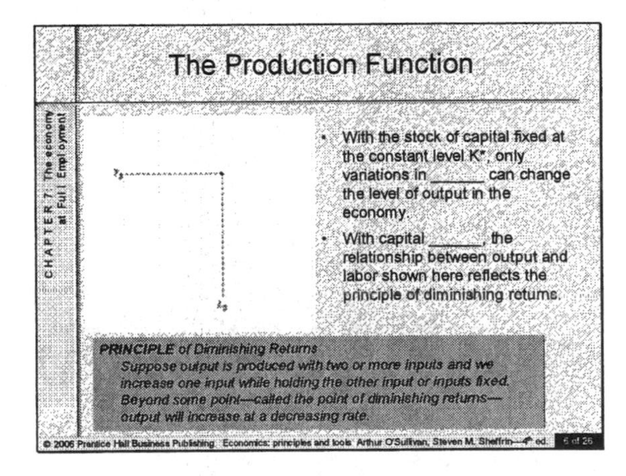
The Production Function
CHAPTER 7: The economy at Full Employment
• With the stock of capital fixed at the constant level K*, only variations in ______ can change the level of output in the economy.
• With capital ______, the relationship between output and labor shown here reflects the principle of diminishing returns.
PRINCIPLE of Diminishing Returns
Suppose output is produced with two or more inputs and we increase one input while holding the other input or inputs fixed. Beyond some point—called the point of diminishing returns—output will increase at a decreasing rate.
© 2006 Prentice Hall Business Publishing Economics: principles and tools Arthur O'Sullivan, Steven M. Sheffrin—4th ed.
6 of 26

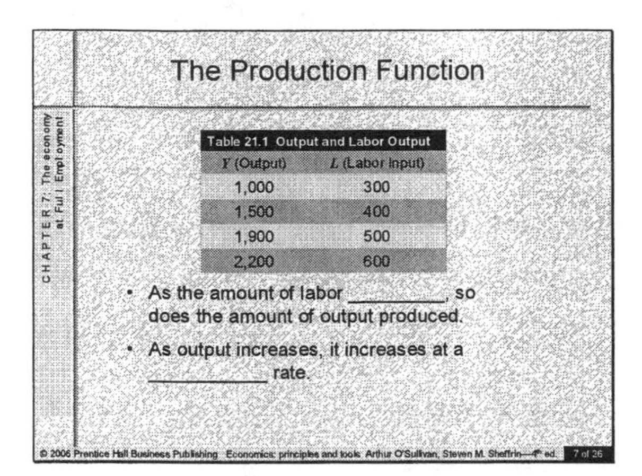

The Production Function

CHAPTER 7: The economy at Full Employment

- When capital increases from K^* to K^{**}, the production function _____ up.
- At any level of labor input, more output can be produced than before the stock of _______ was increased.

© 2006 Prentice Hall Business Publishing Economics: principles and tools Arthur O'Sullivan, Steven M. Sheffrin—4th ed.

Wages and the Demand and Supply for Labor

CHAPTER 7: The economy at Full Employment

- The amount of employment in an economy is determined by the demand and supply for _______.
- The amount of labor firms will hire depends on the _____ **wage**: The wage rate paid to employees adjusted for changes in the price level.
- To understand the demand for labor, we use the marginal principle.

Marginal PRINCIPLE
Increase the level of an activity if its marginal benefit exceeds its marginal cost; reduce the level of an activity if its marginal cost exceeds its marginal benefit. If possible, pick the level at which the activity's marginal benefit equals its marginal cost.

© 2006 Prentice Hall Business Publishing Economics: principles and tools Arthur O'Sullivan, Steven M. Sheffrin—4th ed.

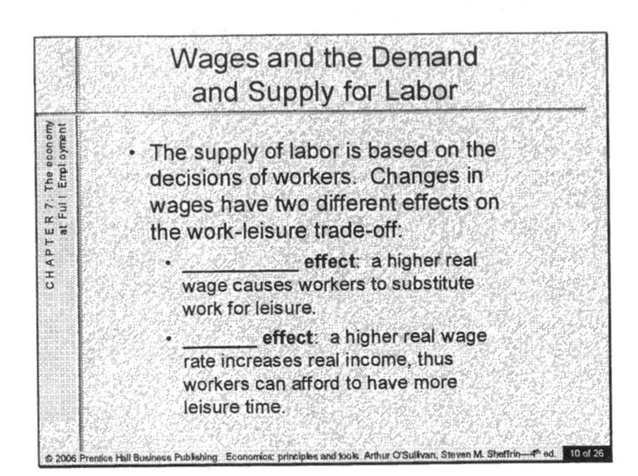
Wages and the Demand and Supply for Labor
CHAPTER 7: The economy at Full Employment
• The supply of labor is based on the decisions of workers. Changes in wages have two different effects on the work-leisure trade-off:
• __________ effect: a higher real wage causes workers to substitute work for leisure.
• _______ effect: a higher real wage rate increases real income, thus workers can afford to have more leisure time.
© 2006 Prentice Hall Business Publishing Economics: principles and tools Arthur O'Sullivan, Steven M. Sheffrin—4th ed.
10 of 26

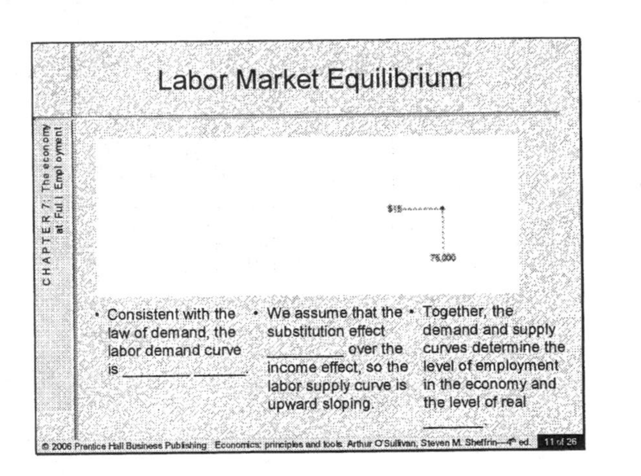
Labor Market Equilibrium
CHAPTER 7: The economy at Full Employment
$15
75,000
• Consistent with the law of demand, the labor demand curve is _______ _______.
• We assume that the substitution effect _________ over the income effect, so the labor supply curve is upward sloping.
• Together, the demand and supply curves determine the level of employment in the economy and the level of real _______.
© 2006 Prentice Hall Business Publishing Economics: principles and tools Arthur O'Sullivan, Steven M. Sheffrin—4th ed.
11 of 26

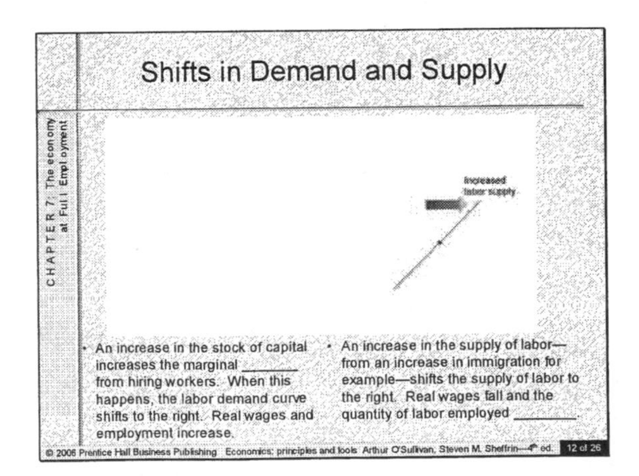
Shifts in Demand and Supply
CHAPTER 7: The economy at Full Employment
Increased labor supply
• An increase in the stock of capital increases the marginal ______ from hiring workers. When this happens, the labor demand curve shifts to the right. Real wages and employment increase.
• An increase in the supply of labor—from an increase in immigration for example—shifts the supply of labor to the right. Real wages fall and the quantity of labor employed _______.
© 2006 Prentice Hall Business Publishing Economics: principles and tools Arthur O'Sullivan, Steven M. Sheffrin—4th ed.
12 of 26

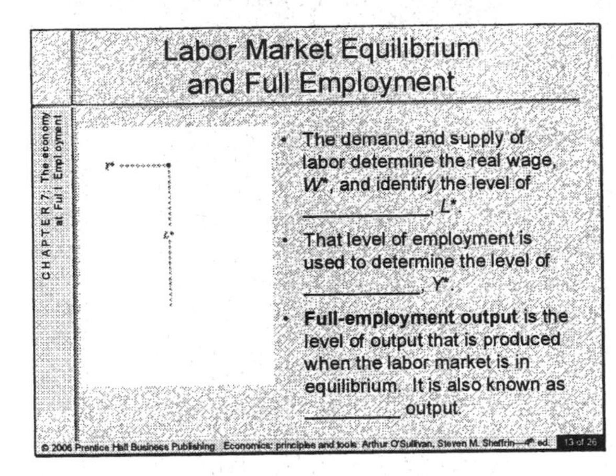

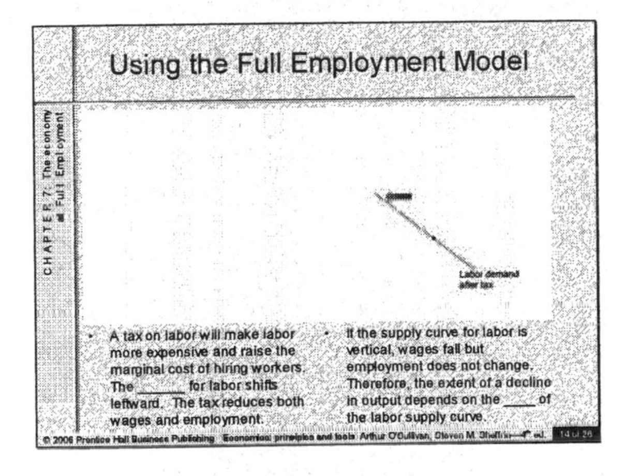

The Laffer Curve

CHAPTER 7: The economy at Full Employment

- The **Laffer curve** is a relationship between tax rate and tax ________ that illustrates how higher tax rates may not always lead to higher tax revenues if the high tax rates discourage economic activity.
- For certain types of taxes, such as income and payroll taxes, cutting tax rates would simply _______ revenue. The labor supply curve is not sufficiently flat for Laffer's idea to work.

© 2006 Prentice Hall Business Publishing Economics: principles and tools Arthur O'Sullivan, Steven M. Sheffrin—4th ed.

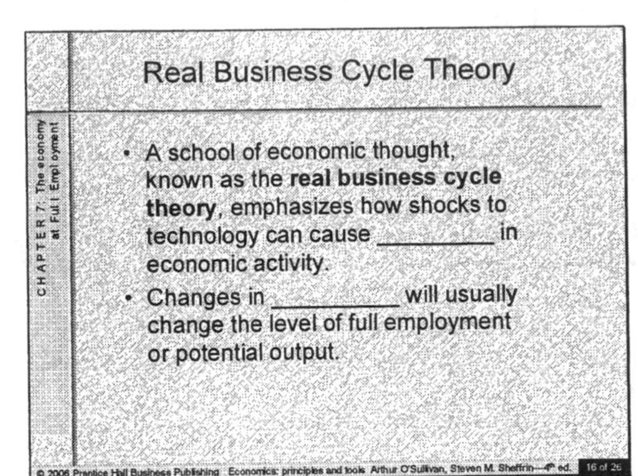
Real Business Cycle Theory
CHAPTER 7: The economy at Full Employment
A school of economic thought, known as the real business cycle theory, emphasizes how shocks to technology can cause _________ in economic activity.
Changes in __________ will usually change the level of full employment or potential output.
© 2006 Prentice Hall Business Publishing Economics: principles and tools Arthur O'Sullivan, Steven M. Sheffrin—4th ed.
16 of 26

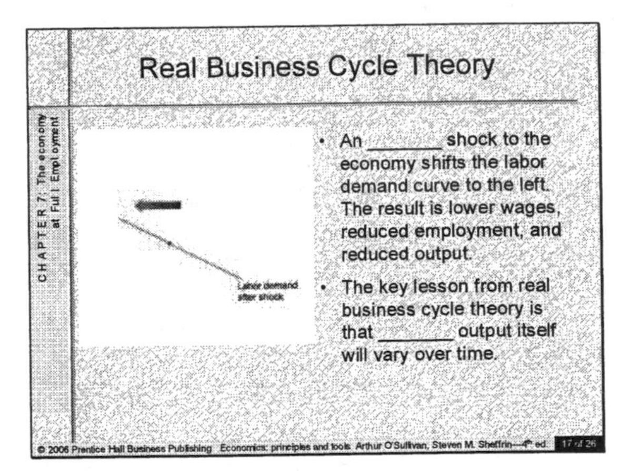
Real Business Cycle Theory
CHAPTER 7: The economy at Full Employment
Labor demand after shock
An _______ shock to the economy shifts the labor demand curve to the left. The result is lower wages, reduced employment, and reduced output.
The key lesson from real business cycle theory is that _______ output itself will vary over time.
© 2006 Prentice Hall Business Publishing Economics: principles and tools Arthur O'Sullivan, Steven M. Sheffrin—4th ed.
17 of 26

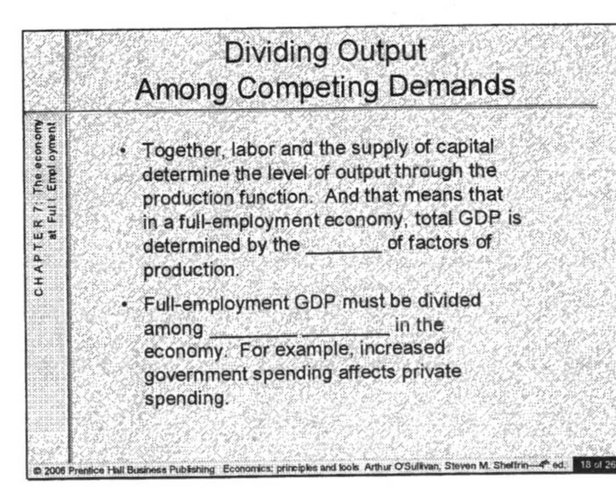
Dividing Output Among Competing Demands
CHAPTER 7: The economy at Full Employment
Together, labor and the supply of capital determine the level of output through the production function. And that means that in a full-employment economy, total GDP is determined by the _______ of factors of production.
Full-employment GDP must be divided among _______ _______ in the economy. For example, increased government spending affects private spending.
© 2006 Prentice Hall Business Publishing Economics: principles and tools Arthur O'Sullivan, Steven M. Sheffrin—4th ed.
18 of 26

Alternative Uses of GDP for 1998 (percent of total GDP)

CHAPTER 7: The economy at Full Employment

Table 21.2 Percentage of GDP Composition, Assorted Countries, 2002

	C	*I*	*G*	*NX*
Japan	57	24	18	1
United States	70	18	16	-4
France	54	20	24	2
Singapore	42	24	12	22
Germany	59	18	20	3

- Consumption (*C*), investment (*I*), and government purchases (*G*) refer to total _________ by residents of that country.

© 2006 Prentice Hall Business Publishing Economics: principles and tools Arthur O'Sullivan, Steven M. Sheffrin—4th ed. 19 of 26

Crowding Out

CHAPTER 7: The economy at Full Employment

- Increased government spending "crowds out" _____ ______ for GDP. This is called **crowding out**. Crowding out illustrates the principle of opportunity cost.

> ***PRINCIPLE** of Opportunity Cost*
> *The opportunity cost of something is what you sacrifice to get it.*

- At full employment, the opportunity cost of increased government spending is some other component of _____

© 2006 Prentice Hall Business Publishing Economics: principles and tools Arthur O'Sullivan, Steven M. Sheffrin—4th ed. 20 of 26

Crowding Out in a Closed Economy

CHAPTER 7: The economy at Full Employment

- An economy without international trade is called a ________ **economy**. In this economy, full-employment output is divided among three different demands:

$$Y = C + I + G$$

- The supply of output (*Y*) is fixed, therefore, increases in government spending reduce, or crowd out, either consumption or investment. In general, ____ are affected.

© 2006 Prentice Hall Business Publishing Economics: principles and tools Arthur O'Sullivan, Steven M. Sheffrin—4th ed. 21 of 26

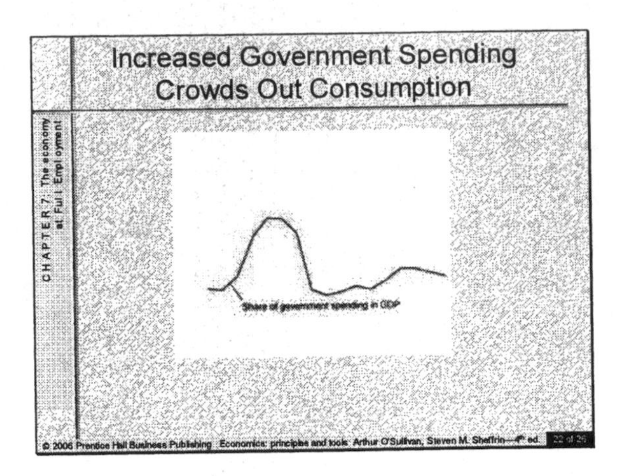
Increased Government Spending Crowds Out Consumption
CHAPTER 7: The economy at Full Employment
Share of government spending in GDP
© 2006 Prentice Hall Business Publishing Economics: principles and tools Arthur O'Sullivan, Steven M. Sheffrin—4th ed.
22 of 26

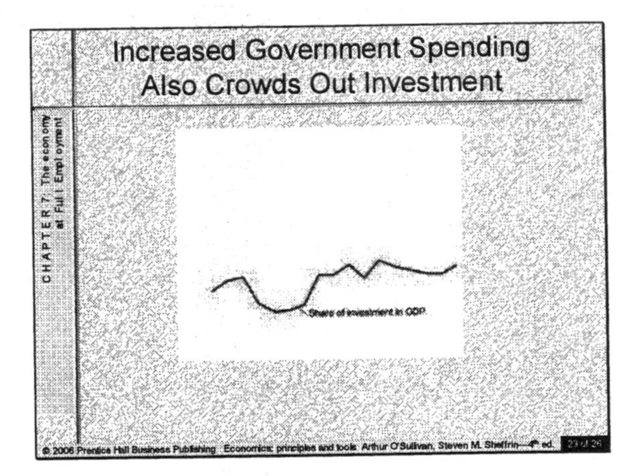
Increased Government Spending Also Crowds Out Investment
CHAPTER 7: The economy at Full Employment
Share of investment in GDP
© 2006 Prentice Hall Business Publishing Economics: principles and tools Arthur O'Sullivan, Steven M. Sheffrin—4th ed.
23 of 26

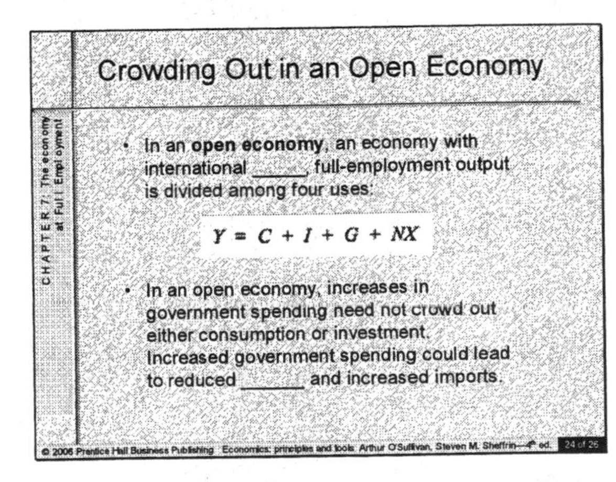
Crowding Out in an Open Economy
CHAPTER 7: The economy at Full Employment
In an open economy, an economy with international _____, full-employment output is divided among four uses:
Y = C + I + G + NX
In an open economy, increases in government spending need not crowd out either consumption or investment. Increased government spending could lead to reduced ______ and increased imports.
© 2006 Prentice Hall Business Publishing Economics: principles and tools Arthur O'Sullivan, Steven M. Sheffrin—4th ed.
24 of 26

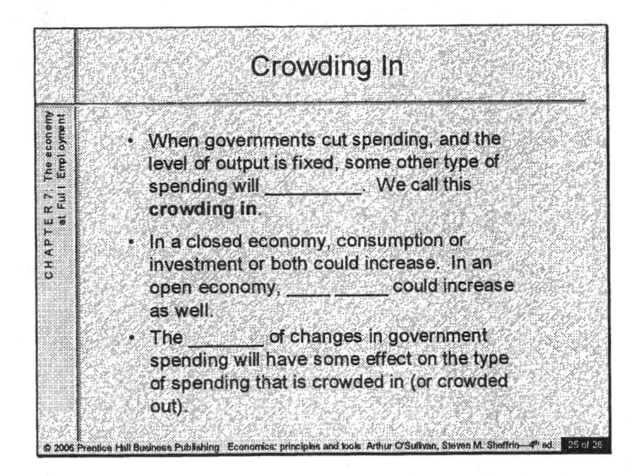

Key Terms

CHAPTER 7: The economy at Full Employment

- classical model
- closed economy
- crowding in
- crowding out
- full-employment output
- income effect
- labor
- Laffer curve
- production function
- open economy
- real business cycle theory
- real wage
- stock of capital
- substitution effect

© 2006 Prentice Hall Business Publishing Economics: principles and tools Arthur O'Sullivan, Steven M. Sheffrin—4th ed. 26 of 26

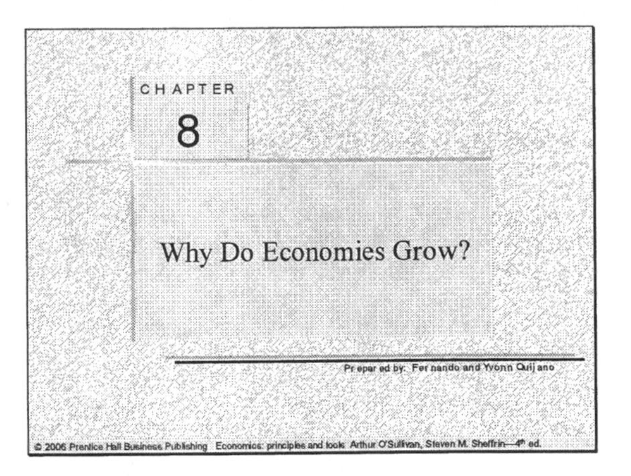
CHAPTER
8
Why Do Economies Grow?
Prepared by: Fernando and Yvonn Quijano
© 2006 Prentice Hall Business Publishing Economics: principles and tools Arthur O'Sullivan, Steven M. Sheffrin—4th ed.

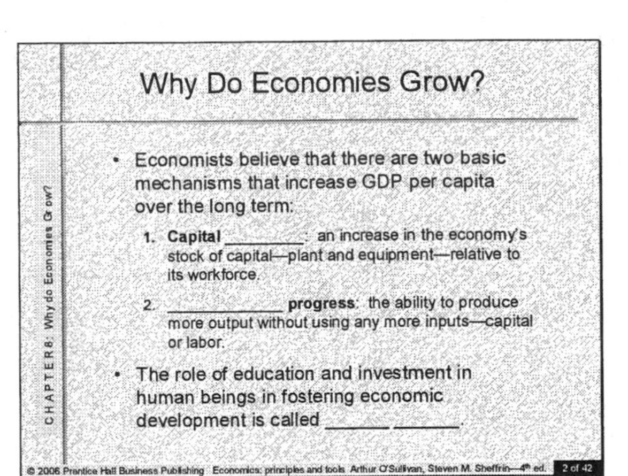
Why Do Economies Grow?
• Economists believe that there are two basic mechanisms that increase GDP per capita over the long term:
1. Capital ________: an increase in the economy's stock of capital—plant and equipment—relative to its workforce.
2. ___________ progress: the ability to produce more output without using any more inputs—capital or labor.
• The role of education and investment in human beings in fostering economic development is called ______ ______.
CHAPTER 8: Why do Economies Grow?
© 2006 Prentice Hall Business Publishing Economics: principles and tools Arthur O'Sullivan, Steven M. Sheffrin—4th ed.
2 of 42

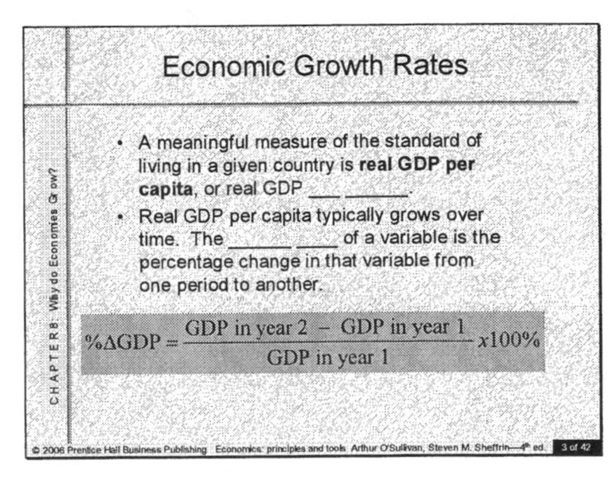
Economic Growth Rates
• A meaningful measure of the standard of living in a given country is real GDP per capita, or real GDP ___ ______.
• Real GDP per capita typically grows over time. The ______ ____ of a variable is the percentage change in that variable from one period to another.
%ΔGDP = (GDP in year 2 − GDP in year 1) / GDP in year 1 x100%
CHAPTER 8: Why do Economies Grow?
© 2006 Prentice Hall Business Publishing Economics: principles and tools Arthur O'Sullivan, Steven M. Sheffrin—4th ed.
3 of 42

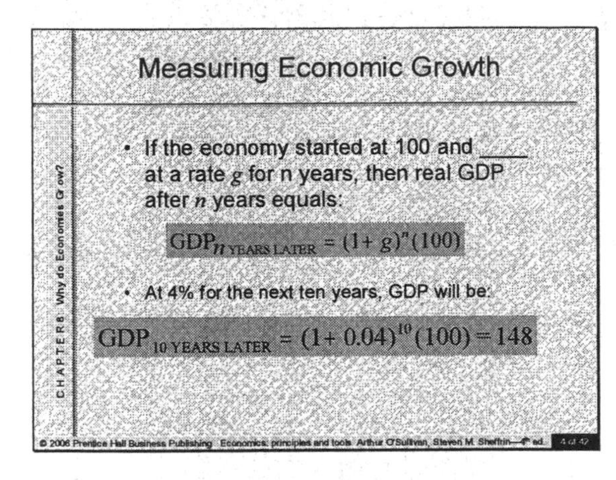

Measuring Economic Growth

- To find out how many years it would take for GDP to double, we use the ____ ____ ____. If an economy grows at x percent per year, output will double in 70/x years.

$$\text{Years to double} = \frac{70}{(\text{percentage growth rate})}$$

CHAPTER 8: Why do Economies Grow?

© 2006 Prentice Hall Business Publishing Economics: principles and tools Arthur O'Sullivan, Steven M. Sheffrin—4th ed.

Comparing the Growth Rates of Various Countries

Table 22.1 GNP Per Capita and Economic Growth

Country	GNP Per Capita in 2001 dollars	Per Capita Growth Rate, 1960-2001
United States	$34,280	2.18%
Japan	25,550	4.16
Italy	24,530	3.07
United Kingdom	24,340	2.17
France	24,080	2.70
Costa Rica	9,260	2.50
Mexico	8,240	2.27
India	2,820	2.43
Zimbabwe	2,220	.82
Pakistan	1,860	.98
Zambia	750	-1.15

CHAPTER 8: Why do Economies Grow?

© 2006 Prentice Hall Business Publishing Economics: principles and tools Arthur O'Sullivan, Steven M. Sheffrin—4th ed.

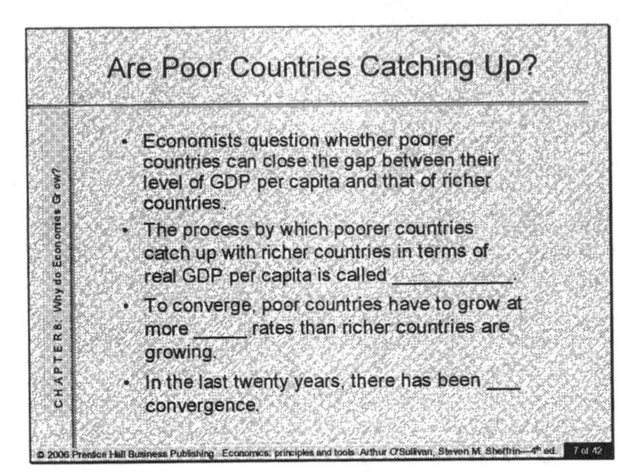
Are Poor Countries Catching Up?
• Economists question whether poorer countries can close the gap between their level of GDP per capita and that of richer countries.
• The process by which poorer countries catch up with richer countries in terms of real GDP per capita is called ___________.
• To converge, poor countries have to grow at more _____ rates than richer countries are growing.
• In the last twenty years, there has been ___ convergence.
CHAPTER 8: Why do Economies Grow?
© 2006 Prentice Hall Business Publishing Economics: principles and tools Arthur O'Sullivan, Steven M. Sheffrin—4th ed.
7 of 42

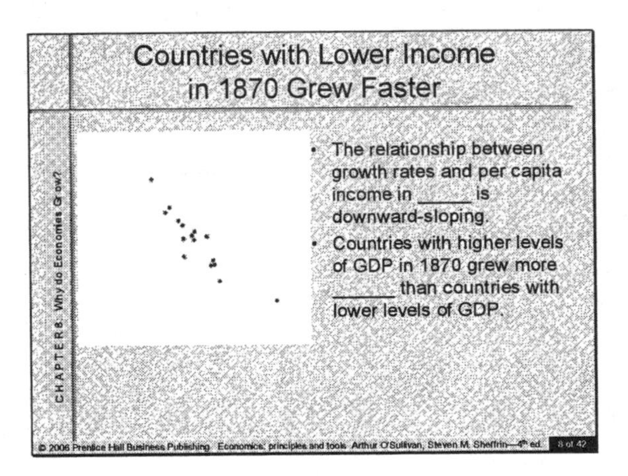
Countries with Lower Income in 1870 Grew Faster
• The relationship between growth rates and per capita income in _____ is downward-sloping.
• Countries with higher levels of GDP in 1870 grew more ______ than countries with lower levels of GDP.
CHAPTER 8: Why do Economies Grow?
© 2006 Prentice Hall Business Publishing Economics: principles and tools Arthur O'Sullivan, Steven M. Sheffrin—4th ed.
8 of 42

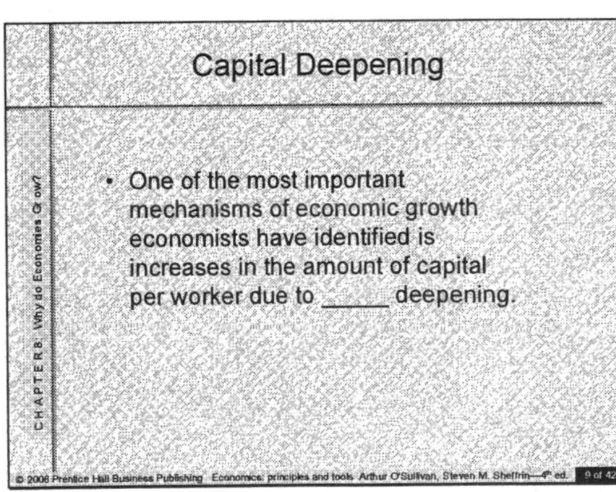
Capital Deepening
• One of the most important mechanisms of economic growth economists have identified is increases in the amount of capital per worker due to _____ deepening.
CHAPTER 8: Why do Economies Grow?
© 2006 Prentice Hall Business Publishing Economics: principles and tools Arthur O'Sullivan, Steven M. Sheffrin—4th ed.
9 of 42

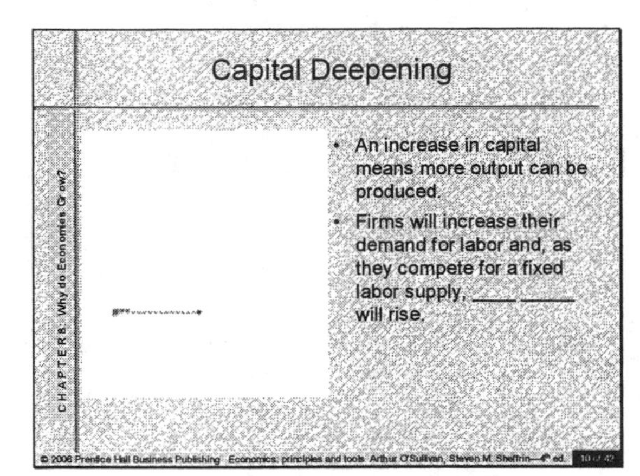
Capital Deepening
An increase in capital means more output can be produced.
Firms will increase their demand for labor and, as they compete for a fixed labor supply, ____ _____ will rise.
CHAPTER 8: Why do Economies Grow?
© 2006 Prentice Hall Business Publishing Economics: principles and tools Arthur O'Sullivan, Steven M. Sheffrin—4th ed.

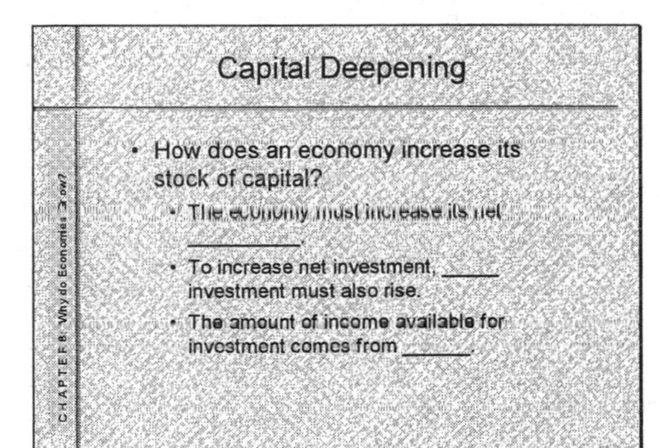
Capital Deepening
How does an economy increase its stock of capital?
The economy must increase its net __________.
To increase net investment, _____ investment must also rise.
The amount of income available for investment comes from ______.
CHAPTER 8: Why do Economies Grow?
© 2006 Prentice Hall Business Publishing Economics: principles and tools Arthur O'Sullivan, Steven M. Sheffrin—4th ed.

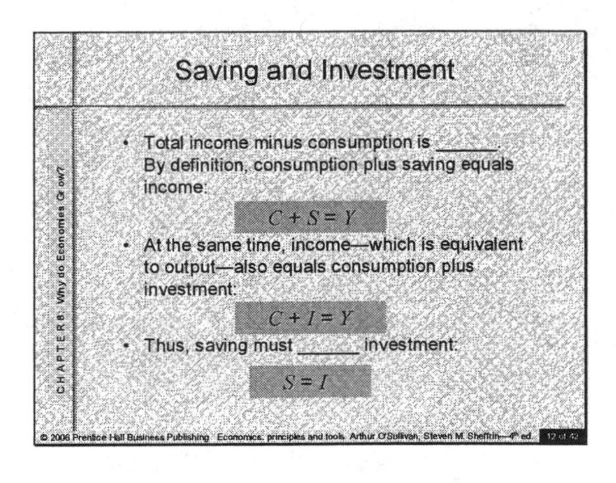
Saving and Investment
Total income minus consumption is ______. By definition, consumption plus saving equals income:
C + S = Y
At the same time, income—which is equivalent to output—also equals consumption plus investment:
C + I = Y
Thus, saving must ______ investment:
S = I
CHAPTER 8: Why do Economies Grow?
© 2006 Prentice Hall Business Publishing Economics: principles and tools Arthur O'Sullivan, Steven M. Sheffrin—4th ed.
12 of 42

Saving and Investment

- This means, whatever consumers decide to save goes directly into investment.
- It follows that in order for the stock of capital to increase, gross investment must exceed ________.
- The stock of capital increases with any _____ investment spending but decreases with any depreciation.
- However, as capital grows, depreciation also grows, eventually ________ to the level of gross investment, and putting a stop to the growth of capital deepening.

© 2006 Prentice Hall Business Publishing Economics: principles and tools Arthur O'Sullivan, Steven M. Sheffrin—4th ed.

How Does Population Growth Affect Capital Deepening?

- ________ growth, which increases the size of the labor force, will cause the capital per worker ratio to decrease.
- With _____ capital per worker, output per worker will also tend to be less because each worker has fewer machines to use. This is an illustration of the principle of diminishing returns.

***PRINCIPLE** of Diminishing Returns*

Suppose output is produced with two or more inputs and we increase one input while holding the other input or inputs fixed. Beyond some point—called the point of diminishing returns—output will increase at a decreasing rate.

© 2006 Prentice Hall Business Publishing Economics: principles and tools Arthur O'Sullivan, Steven M. Sheffrin—4th ed.

How Does the Government Affect Capital Deepening?

- The government can affect the _______ of capital deepening in several ways:
  - Higher taxes will reduce total income. Assuming that households save a fixed fraction of their income, an increase in taxes will cause _______ to fall.
  - As the government drains savings from the private sector, the amount of total ________ decreases, and there is less capital deepening.
  - This occurs when the government uses the taxes collected from the private sector to engage in ________ spending, not investment. However, if the government taxes the private sector in order to increase investment, then it will be promoting capital deepening.

© 2006 Prentice Hall Business Publishing Economics: principles and tools Arthur O'Sullivan, Steven M. Sheffrin—4th ed.

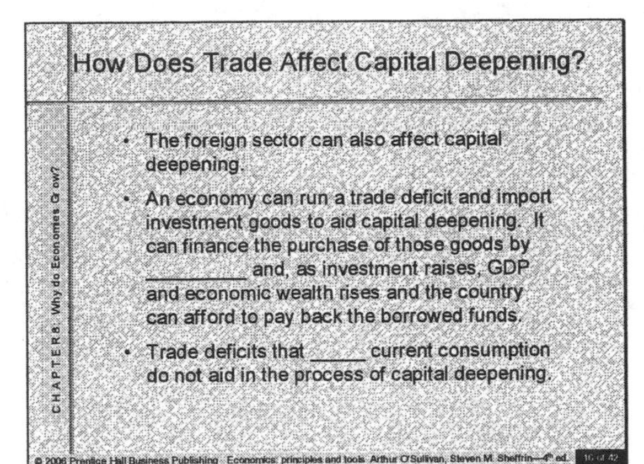

Limits to Capital Deepening

CHAPTER 8: Why do Economies Grow?

- There is a limit to growth through capital deepening because even though at higher _____ _____ _____ can increase the level of real GDP, eventually the process comes to a halt.
- However, it takes time—decades—for this point to be reached. Capital deepening can be an important source of economic growth for a long time.

© 2006 Prentice Hall Business Publishing Economics: principles and tools Arthur O'Sullivan, Steven M. Sheffrin—4th ed. 17 of 42

The Key Role of Technological Progress

CHAPTER 8: Why do Economies Grow?

- Technological progress is the ability of an economy to produce more output _______ using any more inputs.
- With higher output per person, we enjoy a higher standard of living.
- Technological progress, or the birth of new ______ is what makes us more productive. Per capita output will rise when we discover new and more effective uses of capital and labor.

© 2006 Prentice Hall Business Publishing Economics: principles and tools Arthur O'Sullivan, Steven M. Sheffrin—4th ed. 18 of 42

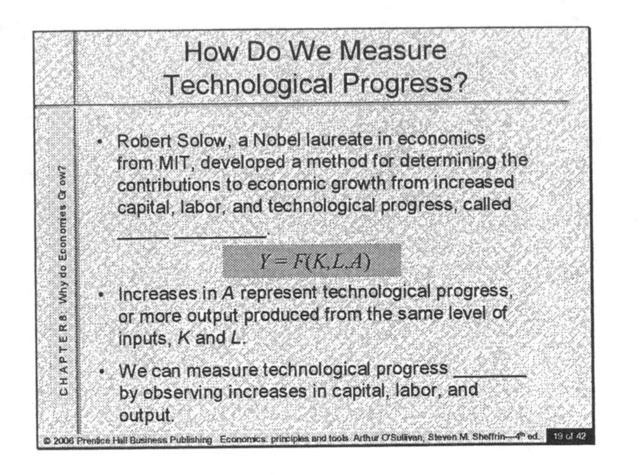

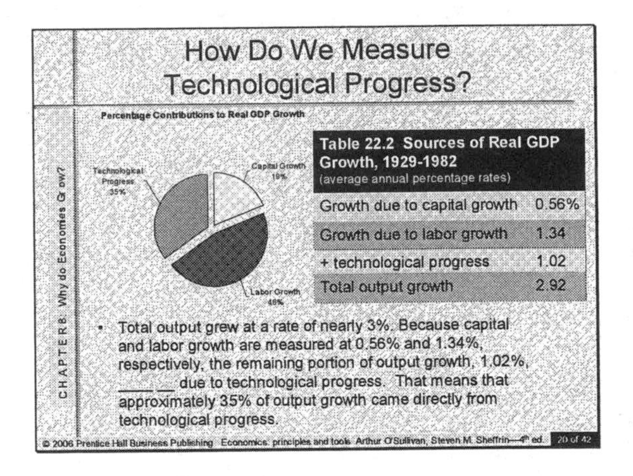

Table 22.2 Sources of Real GDP Growth, 1929-1982 (average annual percentage rates)

Growth due to capital growth	0.56%
Growth due to labor growth	1.34
+ technological progress	1.02
Total output growth	2.92

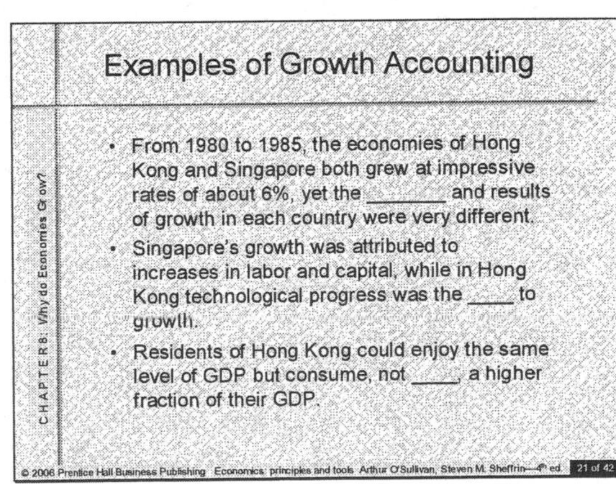

What Caused Lower U.S. Labor Productivity?

- **Labor productivity** is defined as ______ per hour of work for the economy as a whole.
- Labor productivity ________ how much a typical worker can produce with the current amount of capital and given the state of technological progress.
- A significant slow-down in productivity in the United States since 1973 meant slow growth in real wages and in _____.
- In recent years, there has been a resurgence in productivity growth, which reached 2.5% from 1994-2000.

What Caused Lower U.S. Labor Productivity?

Table 22.3 U.S. Annual Productivity Growth, 1959-2002

Years	Annual Growth Rate
1959-1900	0.5%
1966-1973	2.5
1973-1980	1.2
1980-1986	2.1
1986-1994	1.4
1994-2000	2.0

- The period of slower labor productivity growth cannot be explained by reduced rates of capital deepening, nor by changes in the ______ of the labor force.
- A slowdown in technological progress and higher ______ prices have been linked by some economists to the slowdown in productivity.

Real Hourly Earnings and Total Compensation in the United States

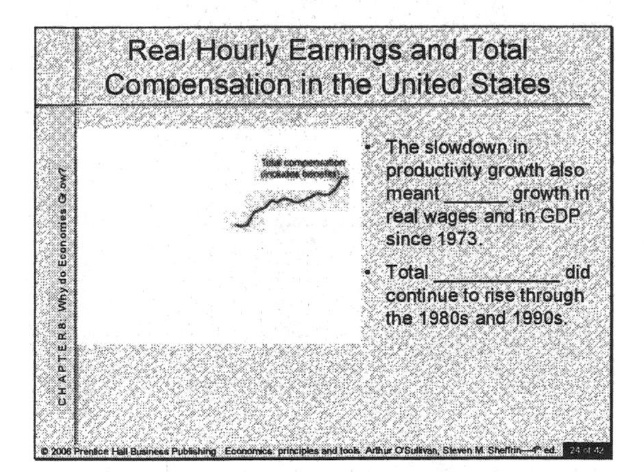

- The slowdown in productivity growth also meant _____ growth in real wages and in GDP since 1973.
- Total ___________ did continue to rise through the 1980s and 1990s.

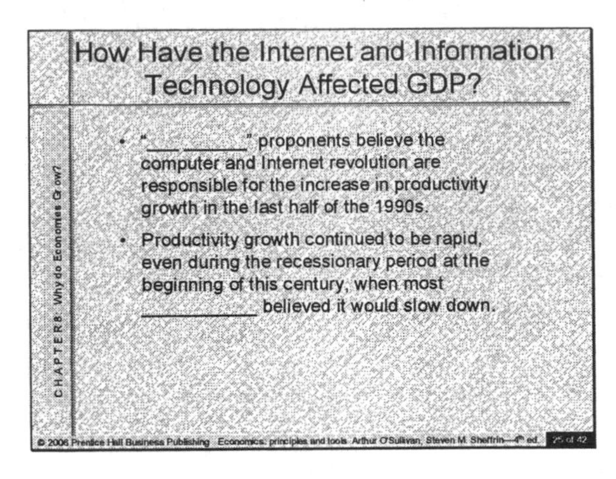

What Causes Technological Progress?

- **Research and development in science.**
  - Government or large firms who employ workers and scientists to advance physics, chemistry, and biology are engaged in technological progress in the ____ ___.
  - The United States has the _______ percentage of scientists and engineers in the labor force in the world.
  - Not all technological progress is "high tech."

CHAPTER 8: Why do Economies Grow?

© 2006 Prentice Hall Business Publishing Economics: principles and tools Arthur O'Sullivan, Steven M. Sheffrin—4th ed. 26 of 42

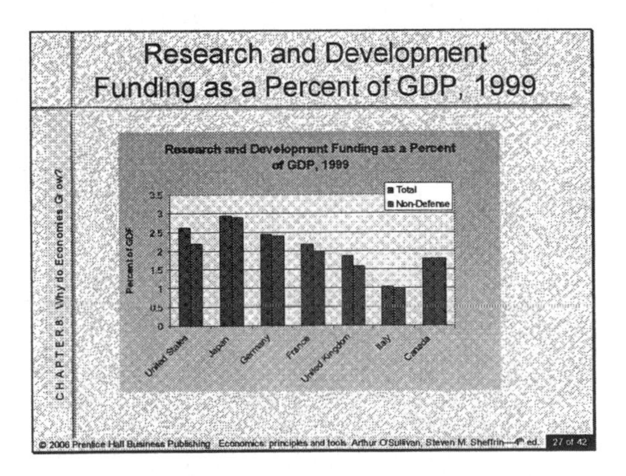

What Causes Technological Progress?

- **Monopolies that spur innovation** (Joseph Schumpeter).
  - The process by which competition for monopoly profits leads to technological progress is called ______ __________ by Schumpeter.
  - By allowing firms to compete to be monopolies, society benefits from increased _________.

© 2006 Prentice Hall Business Publishing Economics: principles and tools Arthur O'Sullivan, Steven M. Sheffrin—4th ed.

CHAPTER 8: Why do Economies Grow?

What Causes Technological Progress?

- **The _____ of the market.**
  - Adam Smith stressed the importance of the size of a market for economic development.
  - There are more _________ for firms to come up with new products and methods of production in larger markets.

© 2006 Prentice Hall Business Publishing Economics: principles and tools Arthur O'Sullivan, Steven M. Sheffrin—4th ed.

CHAPTER 8: Why do Economies Grow?

What Causes Technological Progress?

- _________ **innovations.**
  - Some economists emphasize that innovations come about through inventive activity designed specifically to reduce costs.
- **Education and the accumulation of knowledge.**
  - Modern theories of growth that try to explain the origins of technological progress are know as ____ ______ theory.

© 2006 Prentice Hall Business Publishing Economics: principles and tools Arthur O'Sullivan, Steven M. Sheffrin—4th ed.

CHAPTER 8: Why do Economies Grow?

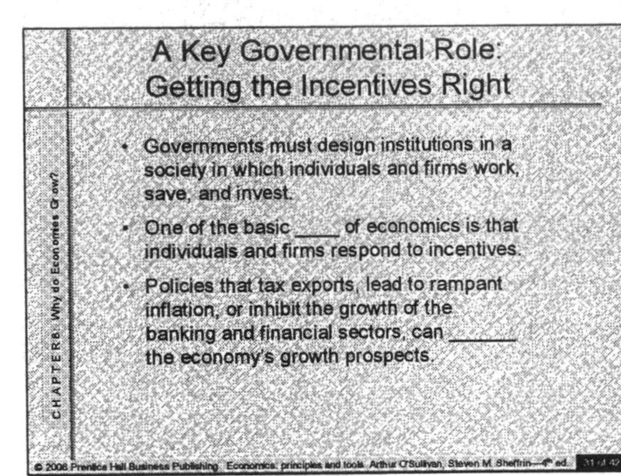

Human Capital

CHAPTER 8: Why do Economies Grow?

- **Human capital** is an investment in human beings—in their knowledge, skills and health.
- In terms of understanding economic growth, human capital __________ has two implications:
  - Not all labor is equal. Individuals with more education will, on average, be more _________.
  - Health and fitness affect productivity. If workers are ____ and ill, they can't contribute much to national output.

New Growth Theory

CHAPTER 8: Why do Economies Grow?

- The work of economists that developed models of growth that contained technological progress as essential features came to be known as **new growth theory**, which accounts for technological _________ within a model of growth.
- Economists in this field study how incentives for research and development, new product development, or international trade interact with the ___________ of physical capital.

Appendix: A Model of Capital Deepening

CHAPTER 8. Why do Economies Grow?

- The ______ model shows that:
  - Capital deepening, the increase in the stock of capital per worker, will occur as long as total saving exceeds depreciation. Capital deepening results in economic growth and increased real wages.
  - Eventually, the process of capital deepening will come to a halt as __________ catches up with total saving.

© 2006 Prentice Hall Business Publishing Economics: principles and tools Arthur O'Sullivan, Steven M. Sheffrin—4th ed.

Appendix: A Model of Capital Deepening

CHAPTER 8. Why do Economies Grow?

- A higher ______ rate will promote capital deepening.
  - If a country saves more, it will have a higher output (until the process of economic growth through capital deepening ends).
- Technological progress not only causes output to increase but also allows capital __________ to continue.

© 2006 Prentice Hall Business Publishing Economics: principles and tools Arthur O'Sullivan, Steven M. Sheffrin—4th ed.

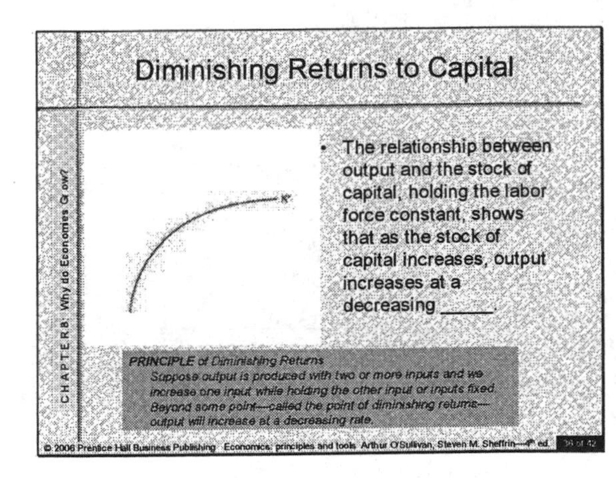

Appendix: A Model of Capital Deepening

- ______ increases with the stock of capital, and the stock of capital increases as long as gross investment exceeds depreciation.
- In the absence of government or the foreign sector, private-sector ______ equals gross investment.
- In order to determine the level of ________, we need to find out how much of output is saved and how much is consumed.

© 2006 Prentice Hall Business Publishing Economics: principles and tools Arthur O'Sullivan, Steven M. Sheffrin—4th ed.

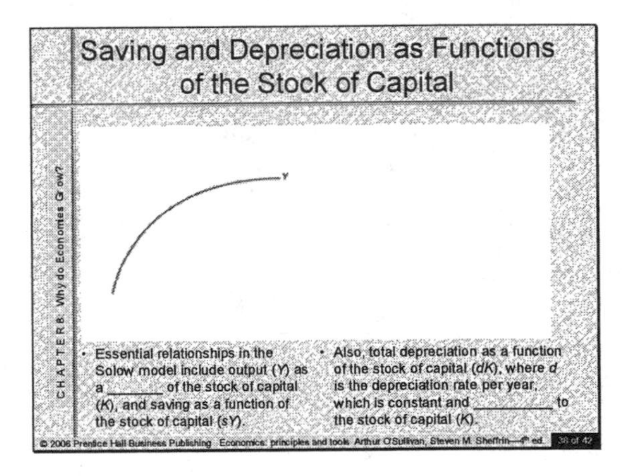

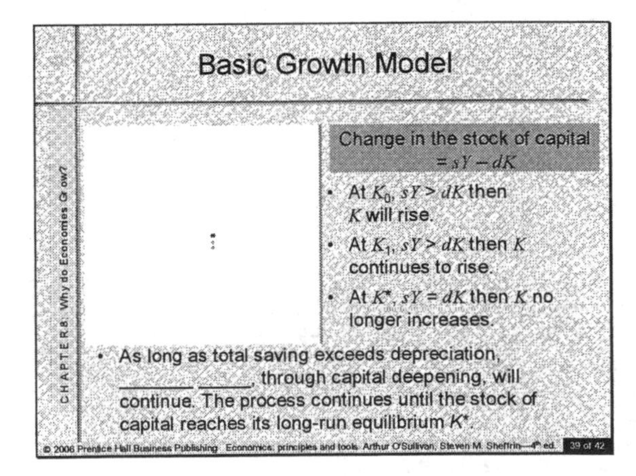

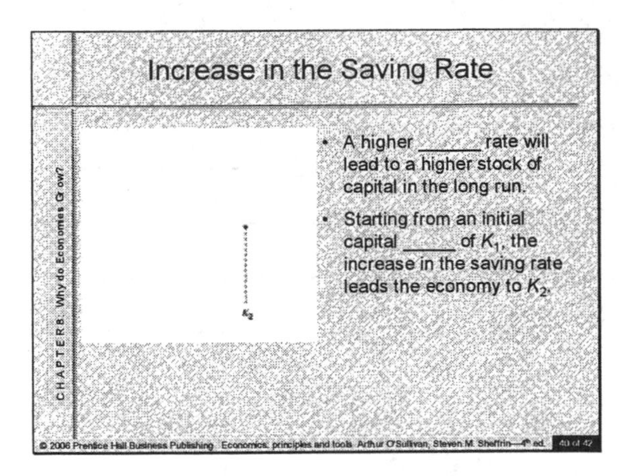
Increase in the Saving Rate
A higher ______ rate will lead to a higher stock of capital in the long run.
Starting from an initial capital _____ of K_1, the increase in the saving rate leads the economy to K_2.
CHAPTER 8: Why do Economies Grow?
© 2006 Prentice Hall Business Publishing Economics: principles and tools Arthur O'Sullivan, Steven M. Sheffrin—4th ed.
40 of 42

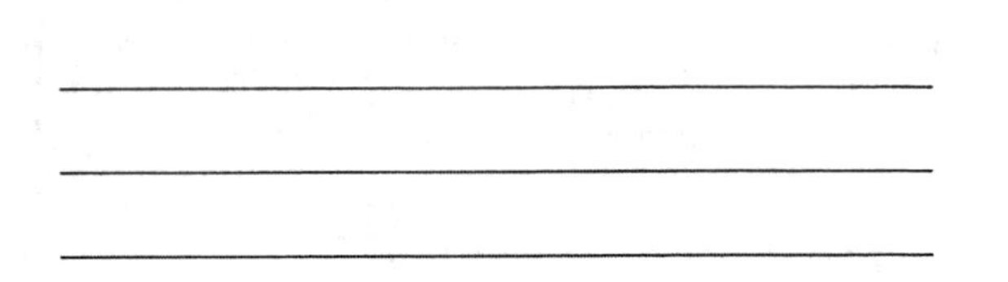

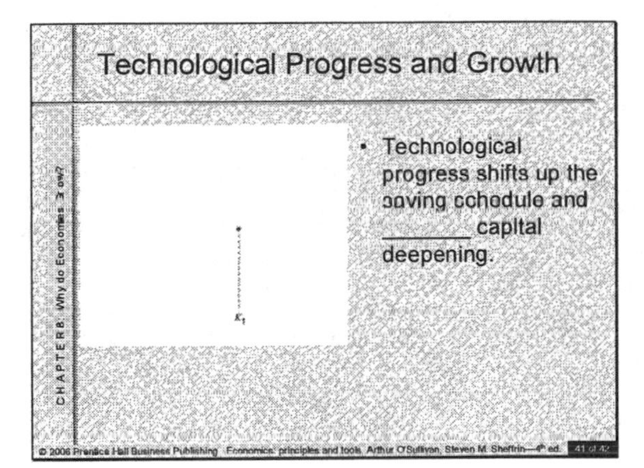
Technological Progress and Growth
Technological progress shifts up the saving schedule and ________ capital deepening.
K_1
CHAPTER 8: Why do Economies Grow?
© 2006 Prentice Hall Business Publishing Economics: principles and tools Arthur O'Sullivan, Steven M. Sheffrin—4th ed.
41 of 42

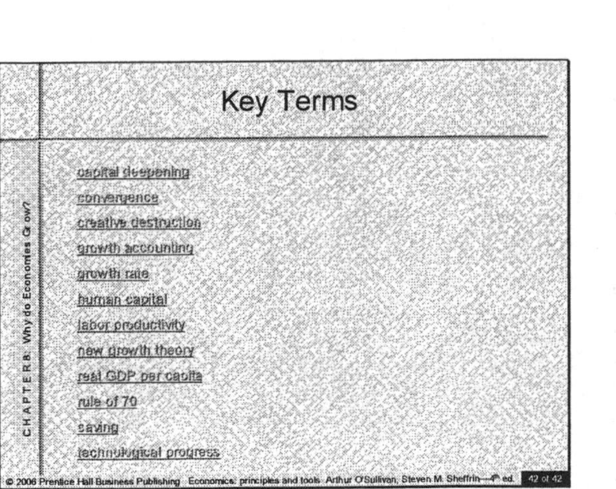
Key Terms
capital deepening
convergence
creative destruction
growth accounting
growth rate
human capital
labor productivity
new growth theory
real GDP per capita
rule of 70
saving
technological progress
CHAPTER 8: Why do Economies Grow?
© 2006 Prentice Hall Business Publishing Economics: principles and tools Arthur O'Sullivan, Steven M. Sheffrin—4th ed.
42 of 42

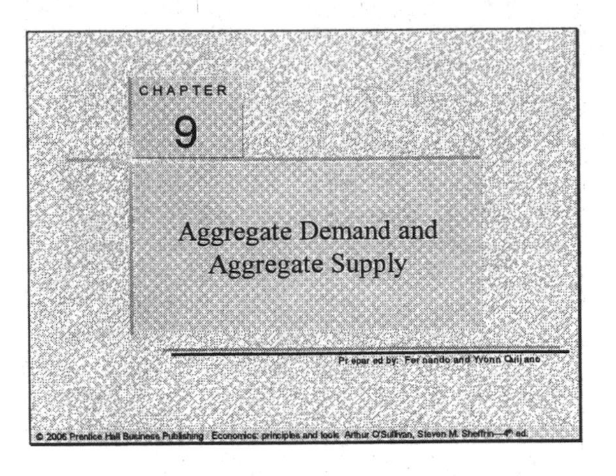

Aggregate Demand and Aggregate Supply

- **Economic fluctuations**, also called **business** ______, are movements of GDP away from potential output.
- Insufficient demand for goods and services was a key problem of the Great Depression, identified by British economist John Maynard ________ in the 1930s.

CHAPTER 9: Aggregate Demand and Aggregate Supply

© 2006 Prentice Hall Business Publishing Economics: principles and tools Arthur O'Sullivan, Steven M. Sheffrin—4th ed.

Sticky Prices and Their Macroeconomic Consequences

- Led by Keynes, many economists since his time have focused attention on economic ____________ problems.
- The price system does not always work instantaneously. If prices are ___ to adjust, then the proper signals are not given quickly enough to producers and consumers.
- In modern economies, some prices (*auctions prices*) are very _______, while others (*custom prices*) are not. Like other input prices, the price of labor adjusts very slowly.

CHAPTER 9: Aggregate Demand and Aggregate Supply

© 2006 Prentice Hall Business Publishing Economics: principles and tools Arthur O'Sullivan, Steven M. Sheffrin—4th ed.

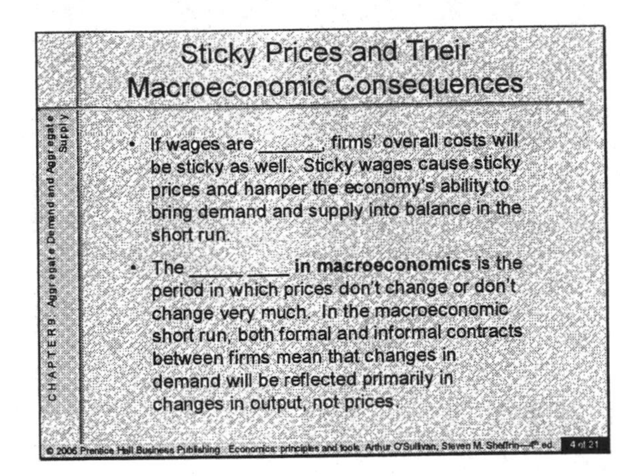

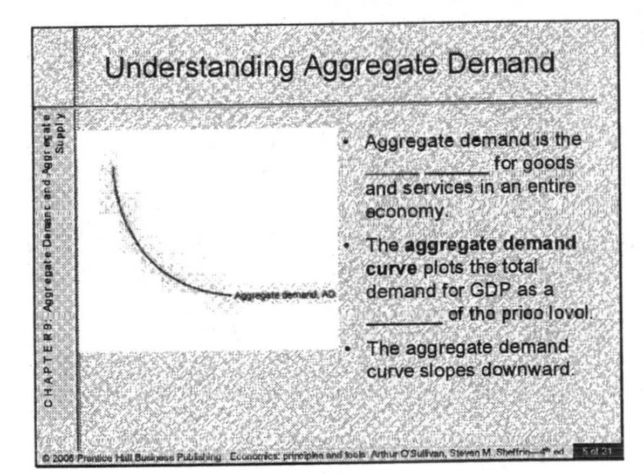

The Components of Aggregate Demand

CHAPTER 9: Aggregate Demand and Aggregate Supply

- In our study of GDP accounting, we divided GDP into four components:
  - Consumption spending (*C*), investment spending (*I*), government purchases (*G*), and net exports (*NX*).
- These four components are also four parts of aggregate demand because the aggregate demand curve really just describes the demand for total GDP at different _____ ______.

© 2006 Prentice Hall Business Publishing Economics: principles and tools Arthur O'Sullivan, Steven M. Sheffrin—4th ed. 6 of 21

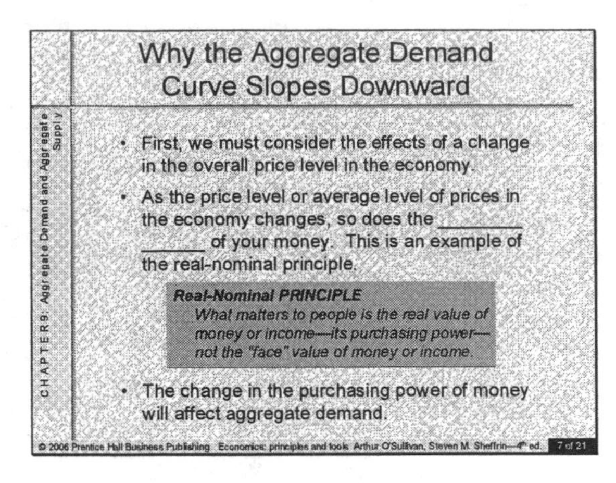

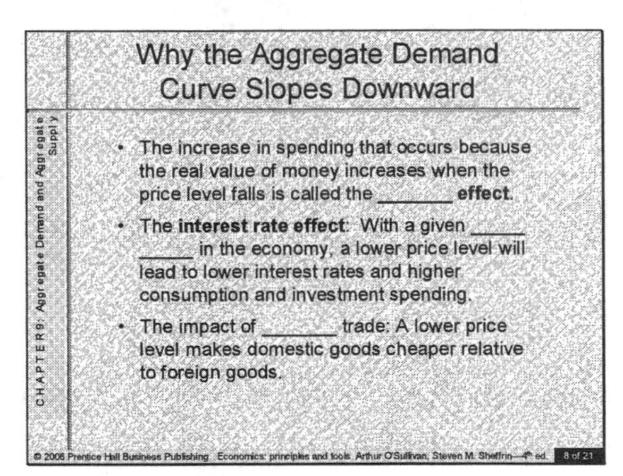

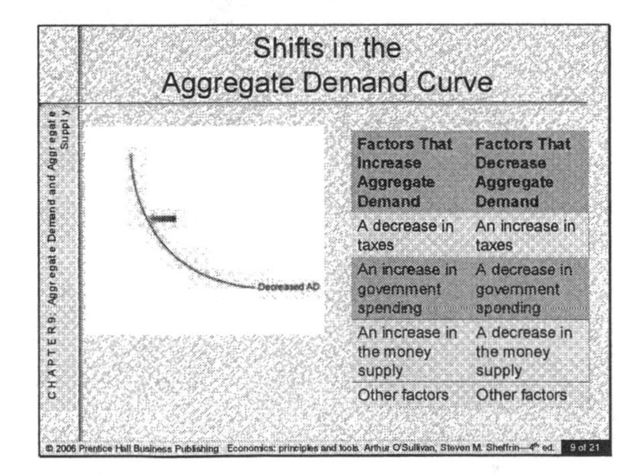

Factors That Increase Aggregate Demand	Factors That Decrease Aggregate Demand
A decrease in taxes	An increase in taxes
An increase in government spending	A decrease in government spending
An increase in the money supply	A decrease in the money supply
Other factors	Other factors

How the Multiplier Makes the Shift Bigger

CHAPTER 9: Aggregate Demand and Aggregate Supply

- The ratio of the final shift in aggregate demand to the initial shift in aggregate demand is known as **the** _________.
- The logic of the multiplier goes back to Keynes. He believed that as government spending increases and the aggregate demand curve shifts to the right, output will subsequently increase too. Increased output also means increased income for households and higher consumption. It is this additional ___________ spending that causes the further shift in the aggregate demand curve.

© 2006 Prentice Hall Business Publishing Economics: principles and tools Arthur O'Sullivan, Steven M. Sheffrin—4th ed. 10 of 21

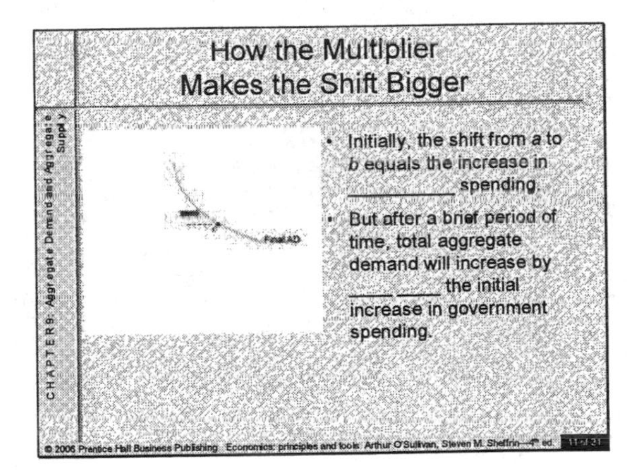

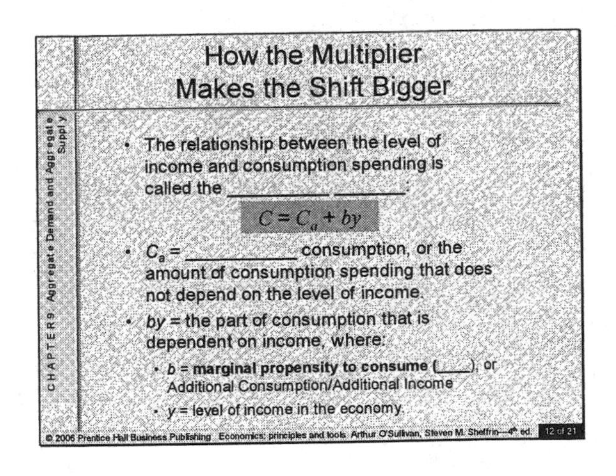

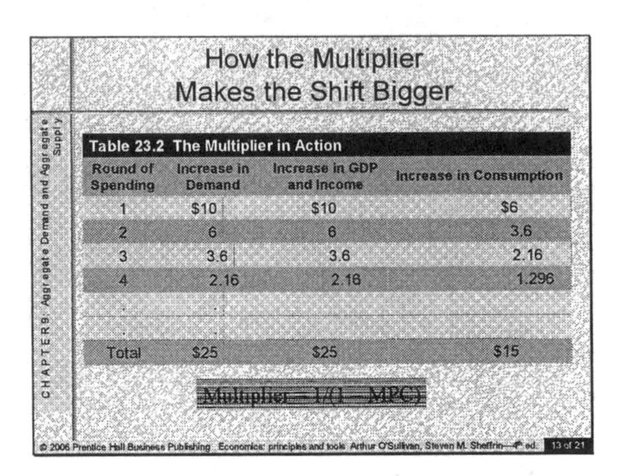

Round of Spending	Increase in Demand	Increase in GDP and Income	Increase in Consumption
1	$10	$10	$6
2	6	6	3.6
3	3.6	3.6	2.16
4	2.16	2.16	1.296
.	.		
.			
Total	$25	$25	$15

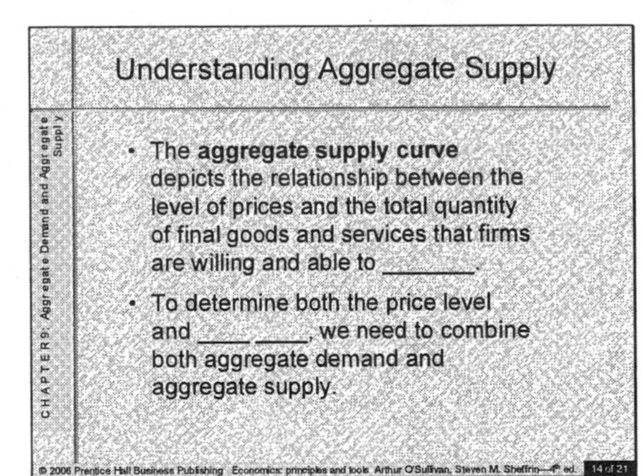

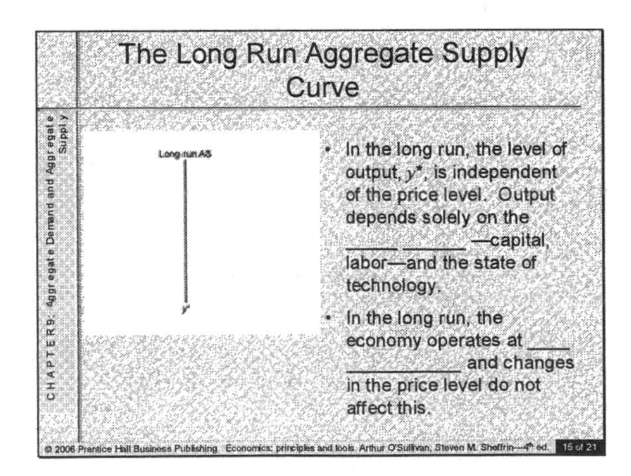

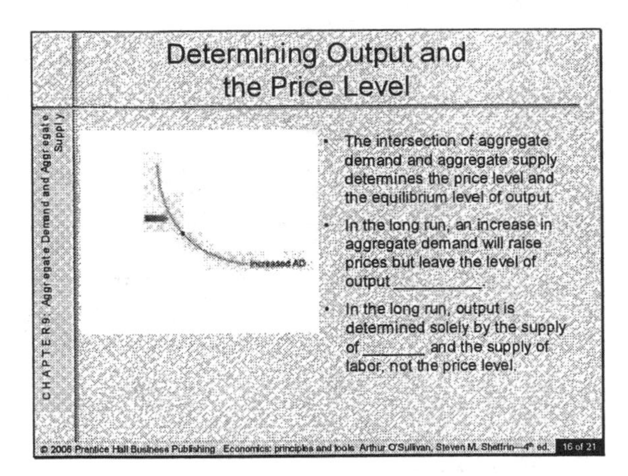
Determining Output and
the Price Level
CHAPTER 9: Aggregate Demand and Aggregate Supply
Increased AD
• The intersection of aggregate demand and aggregate supply determines the price level and the equilibrium level of output.
• In the long run, an increase in aggregate demand will raise prices but leave the level of output ________.
• In the long run, output is determined solely by the supply of ______ and the supply of labor, not the price level.
© 2006 Prentice Hall Business Publishing Economics: principles and tools Arthur O'Sullivan, Steven M. Sheffrin—4th ed. 16 of 21

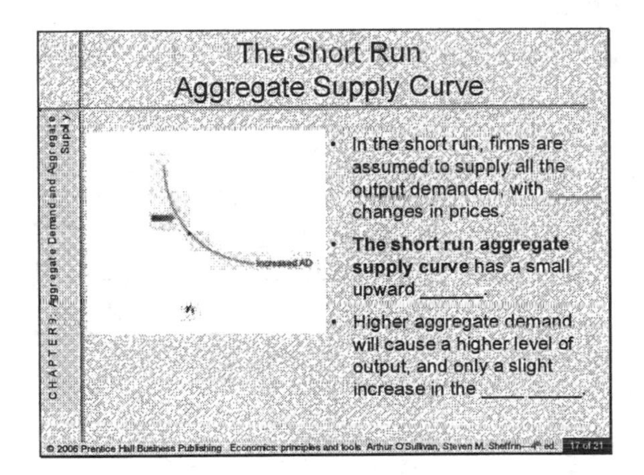
The Short Run
Aggregate Supply Curve
CHAPTER 9: Aggregate Demand and Aggregate Supply
Increased AD
• In the short run, firms are assumed to supply all the output demanded, with _____ changes in prices.
• The short run aggregate supply curve has a small upward ______.
• Higher aggregate demand will cause a higher level of output, and only a slight increase in the _____ _____.
© 2006 Prentice Hall Business Publishing Economics: principles and tools Arthur O'Sullivan, Steven M. Sheffrin—4th ed. 17 of 21

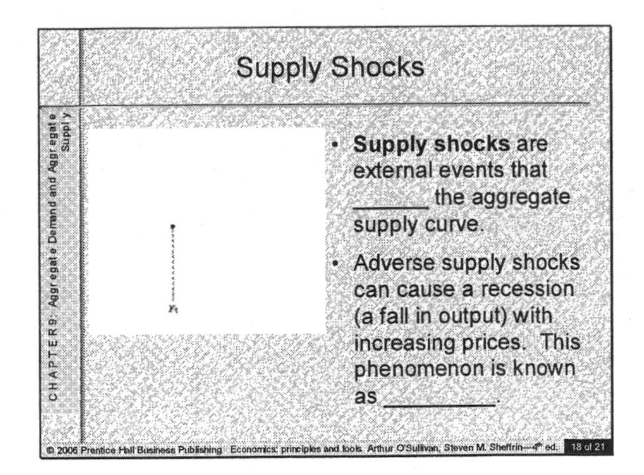
Supply Shocks
CHAPTER 9: Aggregate Demand and Aggregate Supply
• Supply shocks are external events that ______ the aggregate supply curve.
• Adverse supply shocks can cause a recession (a fall in output) with increasing prices. This phenomenon is known as _________.
© 2006 Prentice Hall Business Publishing Economics: principles and tools Arthur O'Sullivan, Steven M. Sheffrin—4th ed. 18 of 21

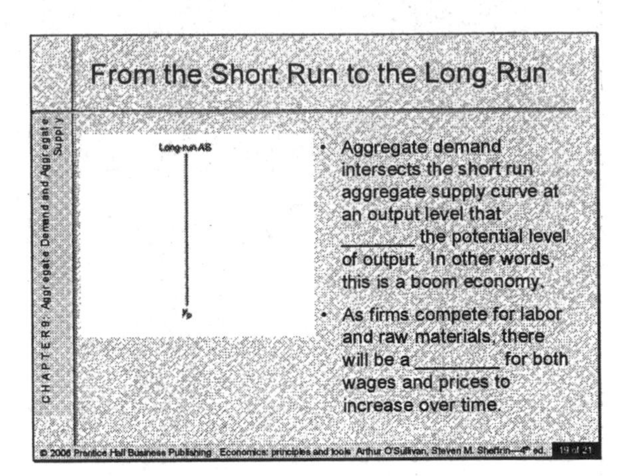
From the Short Run to the Long Run
CHAPTER 9: Aggregate Demand and Aggregate Supply
Long-run AS
• Aggregate demand intersects the short run aggregate supply curve at an output level that ________ the potential level of output. In other words, this is a boom economy.
• As firms compete for labor and raw materials, there will be a ________ for both wages and prices to increase over time.
© 2006 Prentice Hall Business Publishing Economics: principles and tools Arthur O'Sullivan, Steven M. Sheffrin—4th ed.
19 of 21

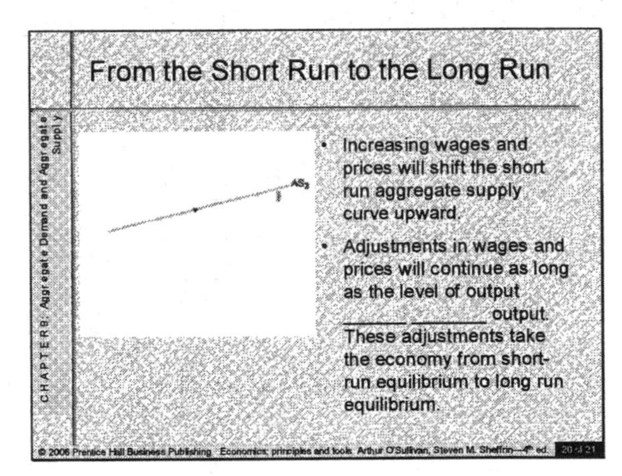
From the Short Run to the Long Run
CHAPTER 9: Aggregate Demand and Aggregate Supply
• Increasing wages and prices will shift the short run aggregate supply curve upward.
• Adjustments in wages and prices will continue as long as the level of output ______ ______ output. These adjustments take the economy from short-run equilibrium to long run equilibrium.
© 2006 Prentice Hall Business Publishing Economics: principles and tools Arthur O'Sullivan, Steven M. Sheffrin—4th ed.
20 of 21

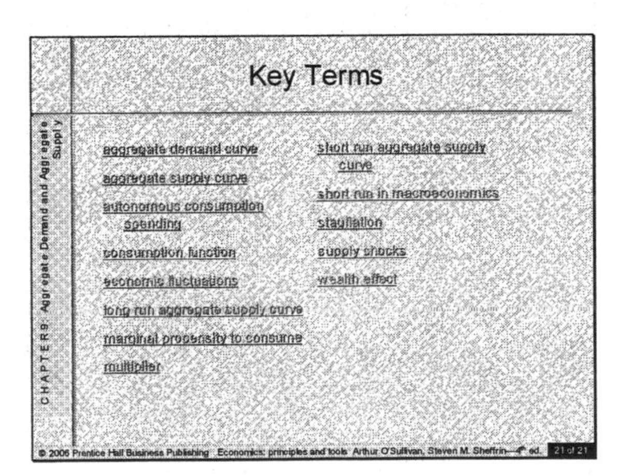
Key Terms
CHAPTER 9: Aggregate Demand and Aggregate Supply
aggregate demand curve
aggregate supply curve
autonomous consumption spending
consumption function
economic fluctuations
long run aggregate supply curve
marginal propensity to consume
multiplier
short run aggregate supply curve
short run in macroeconomics
stagflation
supply shocks
wealth effect
© 2006 Prentice Hall Business Publishing Economics: principles and tools Arthur O'Sullivan, Steven M. Sheffrin—4th ed.
21 of 21

CHAPTER
10
Fiscal Policy
Prepared by: Fernando and Yvonn Quijano
© 2006 Prentice Hall Business Publishing Economics: principles and tools Arthur O'Sullivan, Steven M. Sheffrin—4th ed.

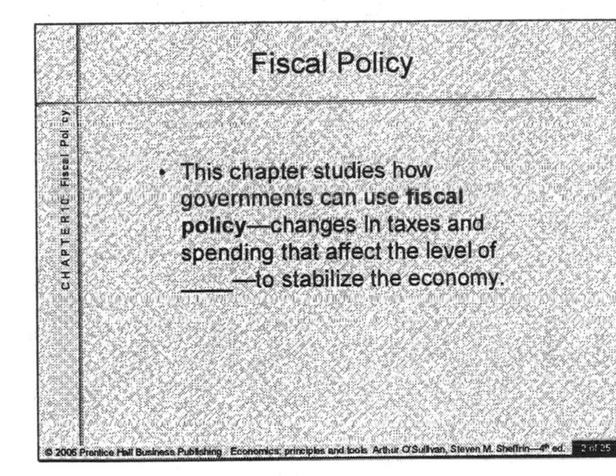
Fiscal Policy
CHAPTER 10: Fiscal Policy
• This chapter studies how governments can use fiscal policy—changes in taxes and spending that affect the level of ____—to stabilize the economy.
© 2006 Prentice Hall Business Publishing Economics: principles and tools Arthur O'Sullivan, Steven M. Sheffrin—4th ed.
2 of 25

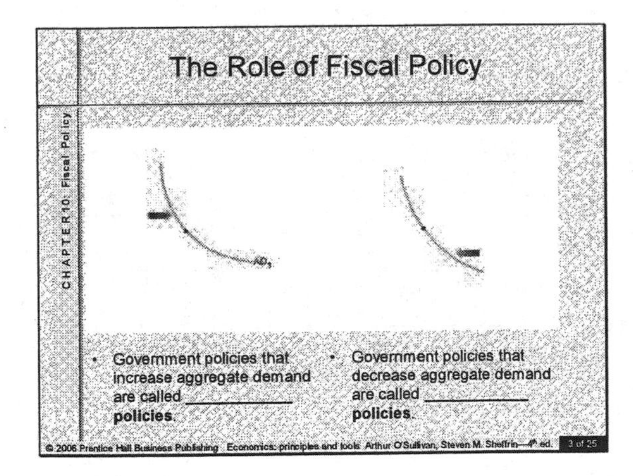
The Role of Fiscal Policy
CHAPTER 10: Fiscal Policy
• Government policies that increase aggregate demand are called __________ policies.
• Government policies that decrease aggregate demand are called __________ policies.
© 2006 Prentice Hall Business Publishing Economics: principles and tools Arthur O'Sullivan, Steven M. Sheffrin—4th ed.
3 of 25

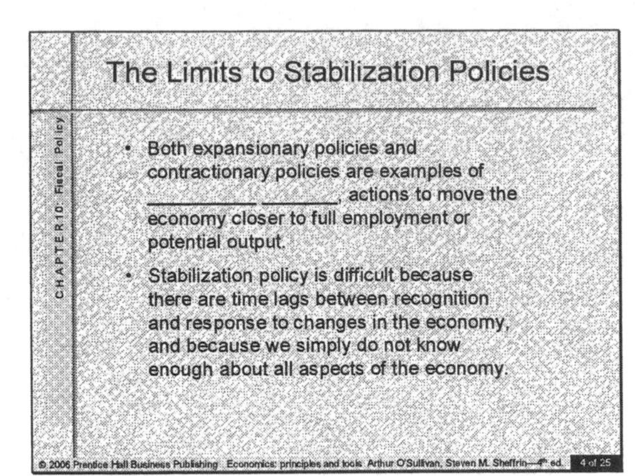
The Limits to Stabilization Policies
CHAPTER 10: Fiscal Policy
• Both expansionary policies and contractionary policies are examples of __________ _______, actions to move the economy closer to full employment or potential output.
• Stabilization policy is difficult because there are time lags between recognition and response to changes in the economy, and because we simply do not know enough about all aspects of the economy.
© 2006 Prentice Hall Business Publishing Economics: principles and tools Arthur O'Sullivan, Steven M. Sheffrin—4th ed.
4 of 25

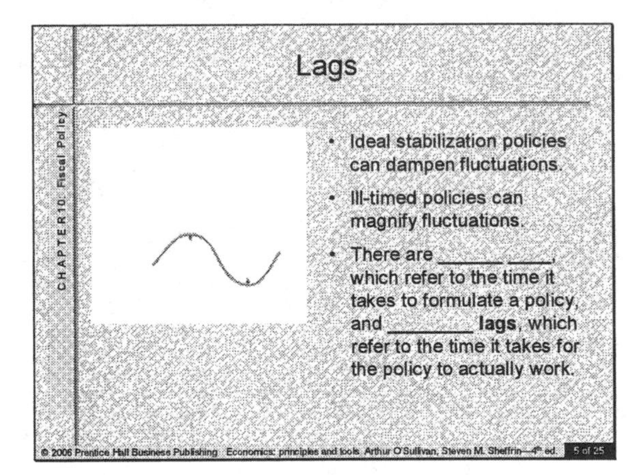
Lags
CHAPTER 10: Fiscal Policy
• Ideal stabilization policies can dampen fluctuations.
• Ill-timed policies can magnify fluctuations.
• There are ______ ____, which refer to the time it takes to formulate a policy, and ________ lags, which refer to the time it takes for the policy to actually work.
© 2006 Prentice Hall Business Publishing Economics: principles and tools Arthur O'Sullivan, Steven M. Sheffrin—4th ed.
5 of 25

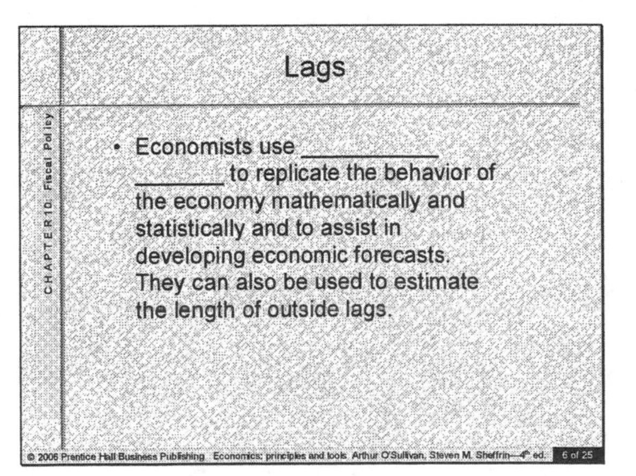
Lags
CHAPTER 10: Fiscal Policy
• Economists use ___________ _______ to replicate the behavior of the economy mathematically and statistically and to assist in developing economic forecasts. They can also be used to estimate the length of outside lags.
© 2006 Prentice Hall Business Publishing Economics: principles and tools Arthur O'Sullivan, Steven M. Sheffrin—4th ed.
6 of 25

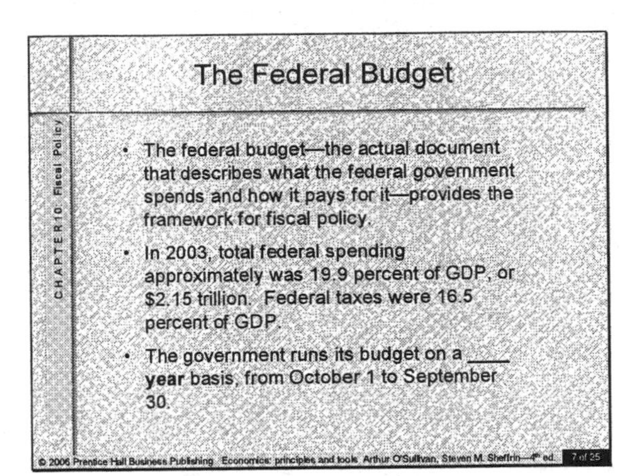

Federal Spending

CHAPTER 10: Fiscal Policy

Table 24.1 Federal Spending for Fiscal Year 2003

Category	Outlays (billions)	Percent of GDP
Total outlays	$2,158	19.9%
Discretionary spending	825	7.6
Defense	405	3.7
Non-Defense	420	3.9
Entitlements and mandatory spending	1,179	10.9
Social Security	470	4.3
Medicare and Medicaid	535	4.9
Other programs	174	1.7
Net interest	153	1.4

© 2006 Prentice Hall Business Publishing Economics: principles and tools Arthur O'Sullivan, Steven M. Sheffrin—4th ed. 8 of 25

Federal Spending

CHAPTER 10: Fiscal Policy

- __________ **spending** constitutes all the programs that Congress authorizes on an annual basis, which are not automatically funded by prior laws passed by Congress.
- **Entitlements and __________ spending** constitutes all spending that Congress authorized by prior laws. They are the single largest component of the federal budget.

© 2006 Prentice Hall Business Publishing Economics: principles and tools Arthur O'Sullivan, Steven M. Sheffrin—4th ed. 9 of 25

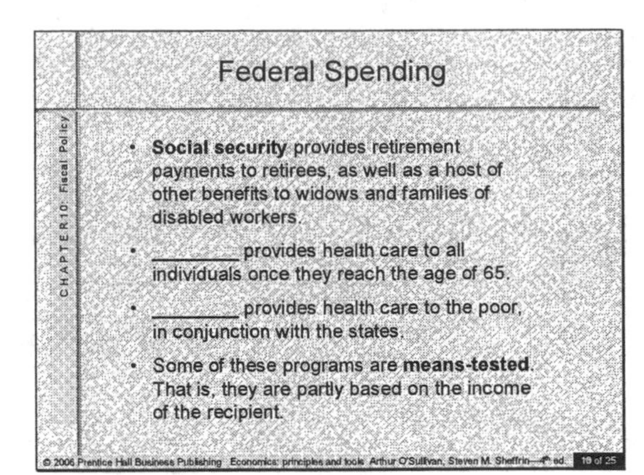

Federal Revenues

CHAPTER 10: Fiscal Policy

Table 24.2 Sources of Federal Government Revenue, Fiscal Year 2003

Category	Receipts (billions)	Percent of GDP
Total revenue	$1,782	16.5%
Individual income taxes	794	7.3
Social insurance taxes	713	6.6
Estate and gift taxes	22	0.2
Corporate income taxes	132	1.2
Excise taxes and customs duties	87	0.8
Miscellaneous receipts	34	0.3

© 2006 Prentice Hall Business Publishing Economics: principles and tools Arthur O'Sullivan, Steven M. Sheffrin—4th ed. 11 of 25

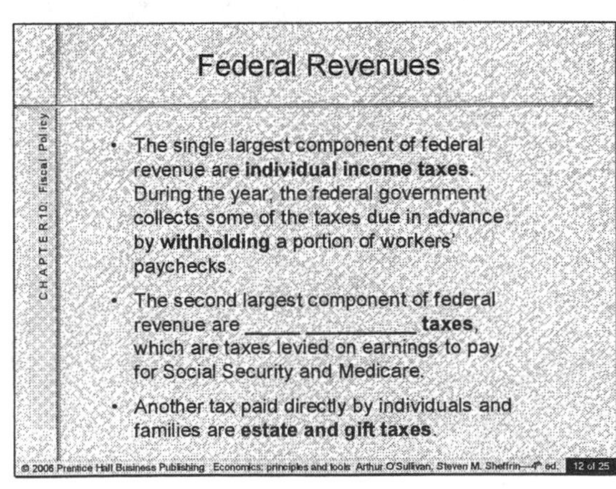

CHAPTER 10: Fiscal Policy

Federal Revenues

- The ________ **tax** is a tax levied on the earnings of corporations. This tax raised less than 7.5% of total federal revenues during fiscal year 2003.
- The other sources of government revenue are relatively minor. ________ ______ **taxes** are taxes levied on the sale of some products, e.g. like gasoline, tires, firearms, alcohol and tobacco. **Custom duties** are taxes levied on goods imported to the United States such as foreign cars or wines.

© 2006 Prentice Hall Business Publishing Economics: principles and tools Arthur O'Sullivan, Steven M. Sheffrin—4th ed. 13 of 25

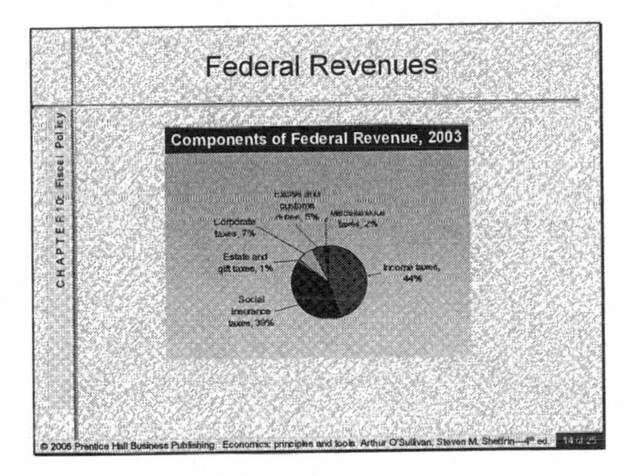

CHAPTER 10: Fiscal Policy

The Federal Deficit and Fiscal Policy

- The federal government runs a **budget** ______ when it spends more than it receives in tax revenues.
- If the government collects more in taxes than it wishes to spend, it is running a **budget** ______. In this case, the government has excess funds and can buy back bonds previously sold to the public.

© 2006 Prentice Hall Business Publishing Economics: principles and tools Arthur O'Sullivan, Steven M. Sheffrin—4th ed. 15 of 25

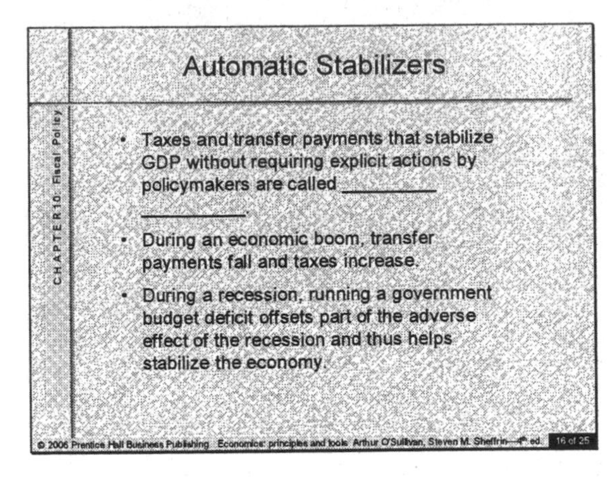

Concerns About Deficits

CHAPTER 10: Fiscal Policy

- In the long run, large budget deficits can have an _________ effect on the economy.
- When the economy is at full employment, a cut in household taxes will tend to increase consumer spending. However, since output is fixed at full employment, some other component of output must be reduced, or crowed out. This is an example of the principle of opportunity cost.

> ***PRINCIPLE** of Opportunity Cost*
> *The opportunity cost of something is what you sacrifice to get it.*

© 2006 Prentice Hall Business Publishing Economics: principles and tools Arthur O'Sullivan, Steven M. Sheffrin—4th ed. 17 of 25

Fiscal Policy in U.S. History

CHAPTER 10: Fiscal Policy

- **The Depression Era**
  - During the 1930s, politicians did not believe in modern fiscal policy, largely because they feared the consequences of government budget deficits. Although government spending increased during the 1930s, taxes increased sufficiently during that same period, with the result that there was no net _____ expansion.

© 2006 Prentice Hall Business Publishing Economics: principles and tools Arthur O'Sullivan, Steven M. Sheffrin—4th ed. 18 of 25

Fiscal Policy in U.S. History

CHAPTER 10: Fiscal Policy

- **The Kennedy Administration**
  - It was not until the presidency of John F. Kennedy during the early 1960s that modern fiscal policy came to be accepted. Walter Heller, the chairman of the president's Council of Economic Advisers under John F. Kennedy, was a forceful advocate of ______ fiscal policy. Kennedy put forth an economic program that was based largely on modern fiscal policy principles. Rapid growth during this period suggests that the tax cuts had the effect predicted by Heller's theory of stimulating economic growth.

© 2006 Prentice Hall Business Publishing Economics: principles and tools Arthur O'Sullivan, Steven M. Sheffrin—4th ed. 19 of 25

Fiscal Policy in U.S. History

CHAPTER 10: Fiscal Policy

- **The Vietnam War Era**
  - As the Vietnam War began and military spending increased, unemployment fell to very low levels. In 1968, a temporary tax surcharge of 10% was enacted to reduce total demand for goods and services. The surcharge did not decrease consumer spending as much as initially estimated because the tax increase was temporary. Consumers often base their spending on an estimate of their long-run average income or ________ **income**, not on their current income. The surtax reduced saving.

© 2006 Prentice Hall Business Publishing Economics: principles and tools Arthur O'Sullivan, Steven M. Sheffrin—4th ed. 20 of 25

Fiscal Policy in U.S. History

CHAPTER 10: Fiscal Policy

- **The Reagan Administration**
  - The tax cuts enacted during 1981 were justified on the basis of improving economic incentives and ________ the supply of output. By the mid 1980s, large government budget deficits began to emerge and policymakers became concerned by them.

© 2006 Prentice Hall Business Publishing Economics: principles and tools Arthur O'Sullivan, Steven M. Sheffrin—4th ed. 21 of 25

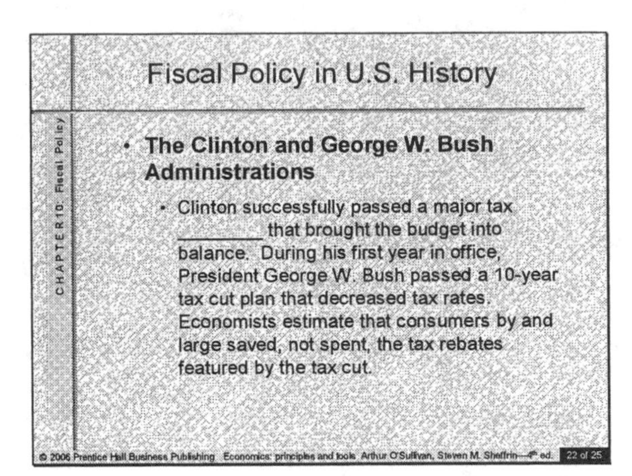

Fiscal Policy in U.S. History
CHAPTER 10: Fiscal Policy
• The Clinton and George W. Bush Administrations
• Clinton successfully passed a major tax ________ that brought the budget into balance. During his first year in office, President George W. Bush passed a 10-year tax cut plan that decreased tax rates. Economists estimate that consumers by and large saved, not spent, the tax rebates featured by the tax cut.
© 2006 Prentice Hall Business Publishing Economics: principles and tools Arthur O'Sullivan, Steven M. Sheffrin—4th ed.
22 of 25

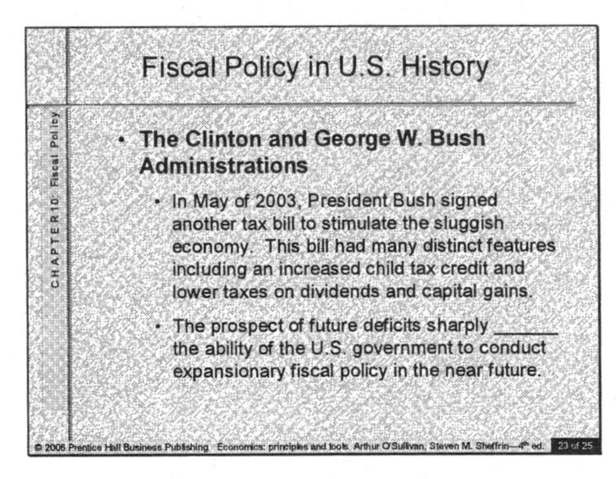

Fiscal Policy in U.S. History
CHAPTER 10: Fiscal Policy
• The Clinton and George W. Bush Administrations
• In May of 2003, President Bush signed another tax bill to stimulate the sluggish economy. This bill had many distinct features including an increased child tax credit and lower taxes on dividends and capital gains.
• The prospect of future deficits sharply ______ the ability of the U.S. government to conduct expansionary fiscal policy in the near future.
© 2006 Prentice Hall Business Publishing Economics: principles and tools Arthur O'Sullivan, Steven M. Sheffrin—4th ed.
23 of 25

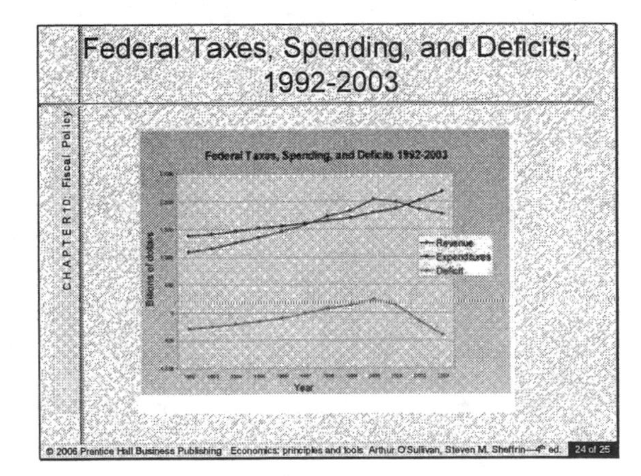

Federal Taxes, Spending, and Deficits, 1992-2003
CHAPTER 10: Fiscal Policy
Federal Taxes, Spending, and Deficits 1992-2003
Billions of dollars
Revenue
Expenditures
Deficit
Year
© 2006 Prentice Hall Business Publishing Economics: principles and tools Arthur O'Sullivan, Steven M. Sheffrin—4th ed.
24 of 25

CHAPTER 1D: Fiscal Policy

Key Terms

- automatic stabilizers
- budget deficit
- budge surplus
- contractionary policies
- corporate tax
- custom duties
- discretionary policy
- econometric models
- entitlement and mandatory spending
- estate and gift taxes
- expansionary policies
- federal excise taxes
- fiscal policy
- fiscal year
- individual income taxes
- inside lags
- means-tested
- Medicaid
- Medicare
- outside lags
- permanent income
- social insurance taxes
- Social Security
- stabilization policies
- withholding

© 2006 Prentice Hall Business Publishing Economics: principles and tools Arthur O'Sullivan, Steven M. Sheffrin—4th ed. 25 of 25

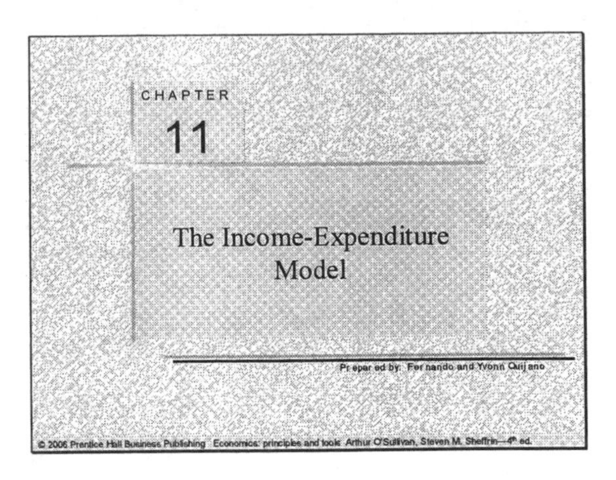
CHAPTER
11
The Income-Expenditure Model
Prepared by: Fernando and Yvonn Quijano
© 2006 Prentice Hall Business Publishing Economics: principles and tools Arthur O'Sullivan, Steven M. Sheffrin—4th ed.

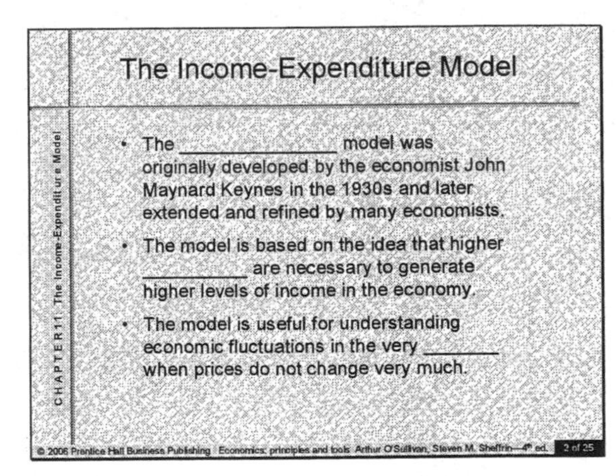
The Income-Expenditure Model
• The ______________ model was originally developed by the economist John Maynard Keynes in the 1930s and later extended and refined by many economists.
• The model is based on the idea that higher __________ are necessary to generate higher levels of income in the economy.
• The model is useful for understanding economic fluctuations in the very _______ when prices do not change very much.
CHAPTER 11: The Income-Expenditure Model
© 2006 Prentice Hall Business Publishing Economics: principles and tools Arthur O'Sullivan, Steven M. Sheffrin—4th ed.
2 of 25

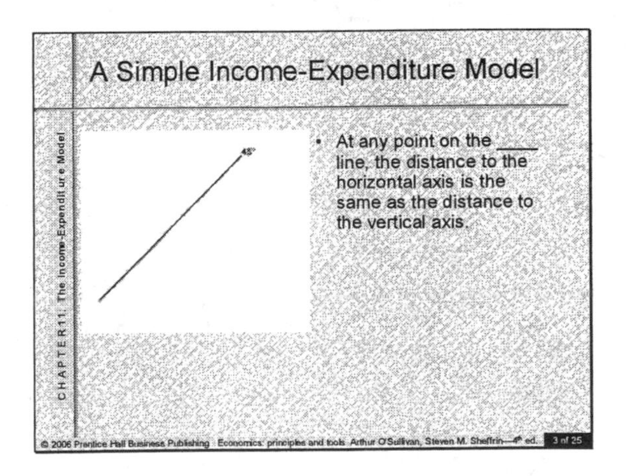
A Simple Income-Expenditure Model
45°
• At any point on the ____ line, the distance to the horizontal axis is the same as the distance to the vertical axis.
CHAPTER 11: The Income-Expenditure Model
© 2006 Prentice Hall Business Publishing Economics: principles and tools Arthur O'Sullivan, Steven M. Sheffrin—4th ed.
3 of 25

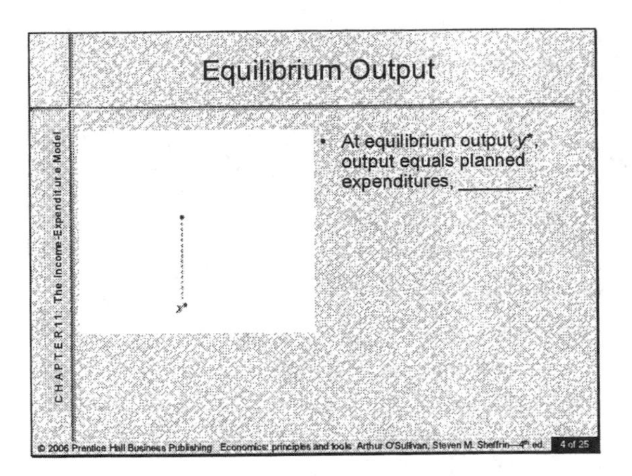

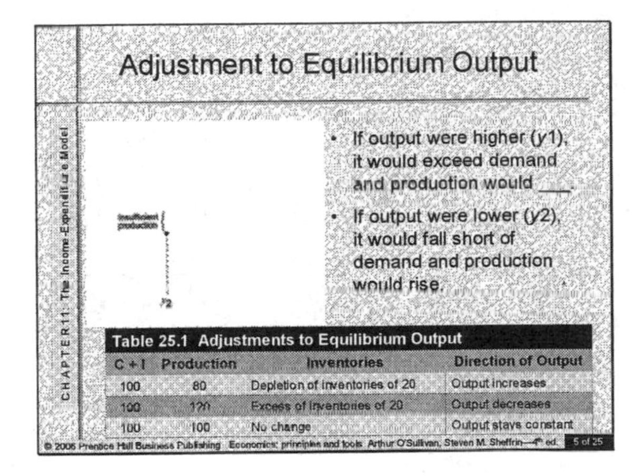

Table 25.1 Adjustments to Equilibrium Output

C + I	Production	Inventories	Direction of Output
100	80	Depletion of inventories of 20	Output increases
100	120	Excess of inventories of 20	Output decreases
100	100	No change	Output stays constant

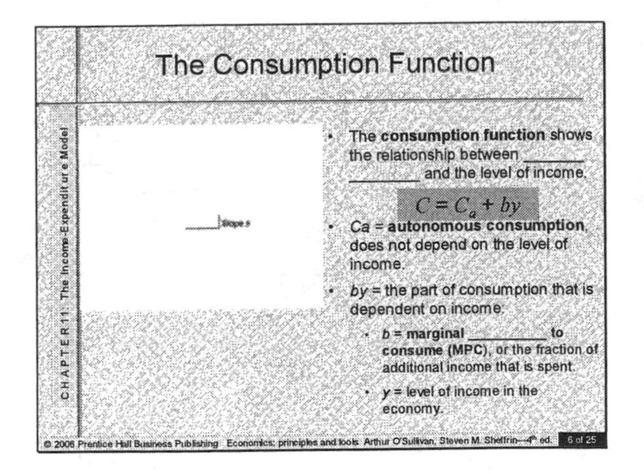

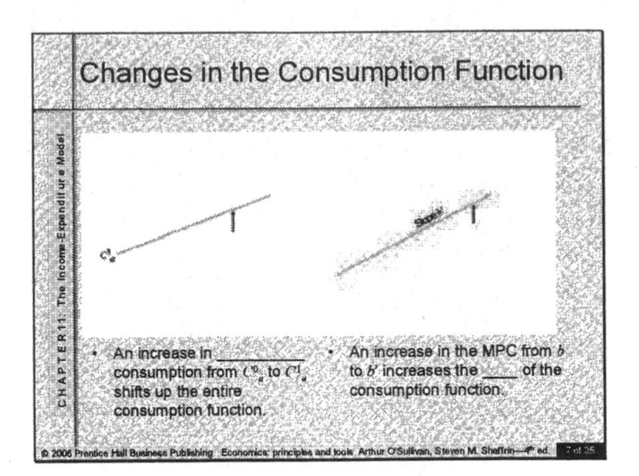
Changes in the Consumption Function
CHAPTER 11: The Income-Expenditure Model
An increase in ________ consumption from C^0_a to C^1_a shifts up the entire consumption function.
An increase in the MPC from b to b' increases the ____ of the consumption function.
© 2006 Prentice Hall Business Publishing Economics: principles and tools Arthur O'Sullivan, Steven M. Sheffrin—4th ed.
7 of 25

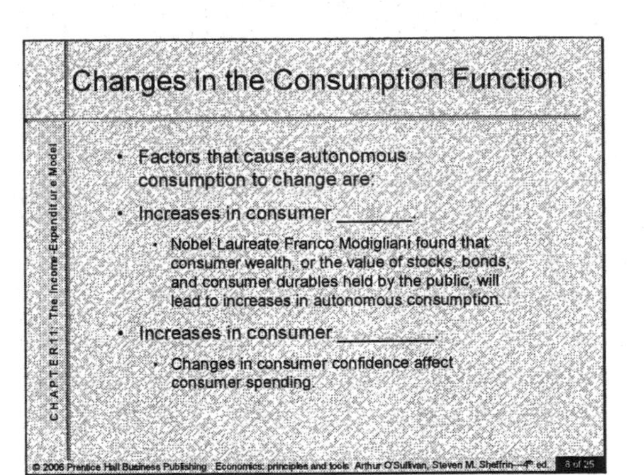
Changes in the Consumption Function
CHAPTER 11: The Income-Expenditure Model
Factors that cause autonomous consumption to change are:
Increases in consumer ______.
Nobel Laureate Franco Modigliani found that consumer wealth, or the value of stocks, bonds, and consumer durables held by the public, will lead to increases in autonomous consumption.
Increases in consumer ________.
Changes in consumer confidence affect consumer spending.
© 2006 Prentice Hall Business Publishing Economics: principles and tools Arthur O'Sullivan, Steven M. Sheffrin—4th ed.
8 of 25

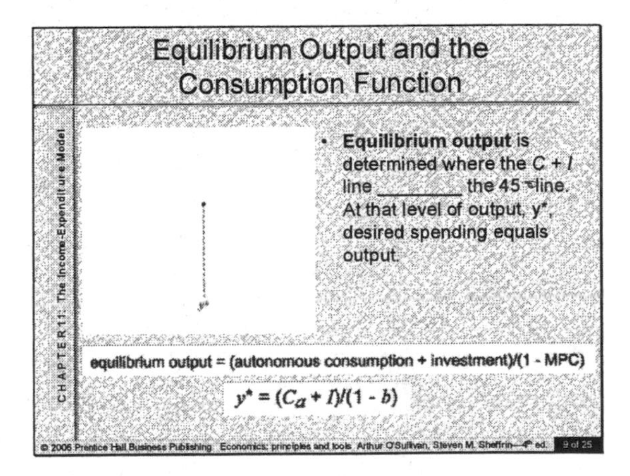
Equilibrium Output and the Consumption Function
CHAPTER 11: The Income-Expenditure Model
Equilibrium output is determined where the C + I line ________ the 45°-line. At that level of output, y*, desired spending equals output.
equilibrium output = (autonomous consumption + investment)/(1 - MPC)
$y^* = (C_a + I)/(1 - b)$
© 2006 Prentice Hall Business Publishing Economics: principles and tools Arthur O'Sullivan, Steven M. Sheffrin—4th ed.
9 of 25

Savings and Investment

- ______ equals output minus consumption.

$$S = y - C$$

- Output is determined by ________, $C + I$, or

$$y = C + I$$

- Subtracting consumption from both sides of the equation results in:

$$y - C = I$$

- The left side shows that $y - C$ equals savings, S, therefore:

$$S = I$$

© 2006 Prentice Hall Business Publishing Economics: principles and tools Arthur O'Sullivan, Steven M. Sheffrin—4th ed.

Savings and Investment

- Equilibrium output is determined at the level of income where savings equals investment.
- The level of savings in the economy is not fixed, and how it changes depends on the real GDP.
- The _______________ is the relationship between the level of income and the level of savings.
- The fraction that the consumer saves is determined by his or her **marginal propensity to save (____)**.

© 2006 Prentice Hall Business Publishing Economics: principles and tools Arthur O'Sullivan, Steven M. Sheffrin—4th ed.

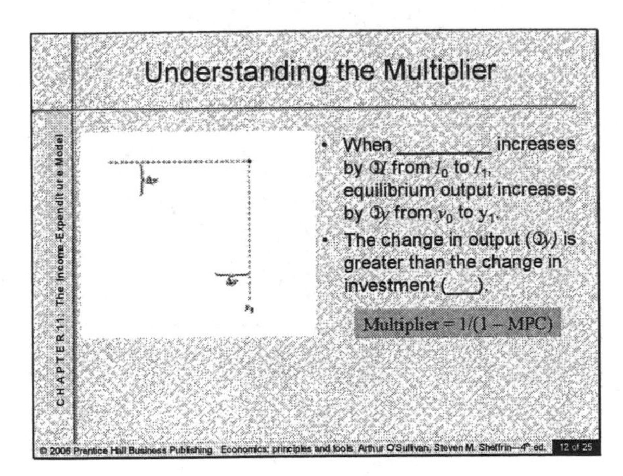

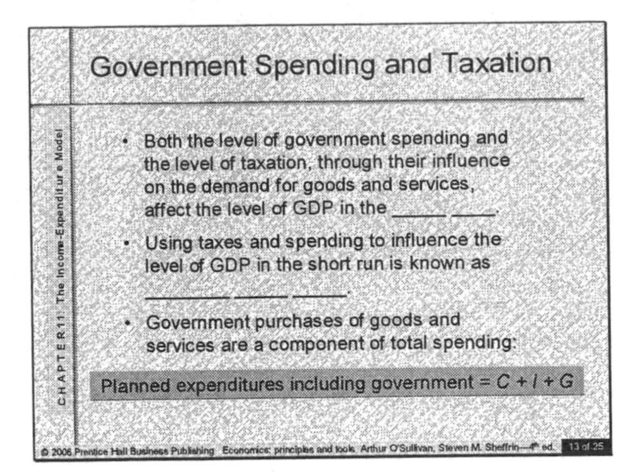

Government Spending and Taxation
CHAPTER 11: The Income-Expenditure Model
Both the level of government spending and the level of taxation, through their influence on the demand for goods and services, affect the level of GDP in the _____ ____.
Using taxes and spending to influence the level of GDP in the short run is known as ________ _____ _____.
Government purchases of goods and services are a component of total spending:
Planned expenditures including government = C + I + G
© 2006 Prentice Hall Business Publishing Economics: principles and tools Arthur O'Sullivan, Steven M. Sheffrin—4th ed. 13 of 25

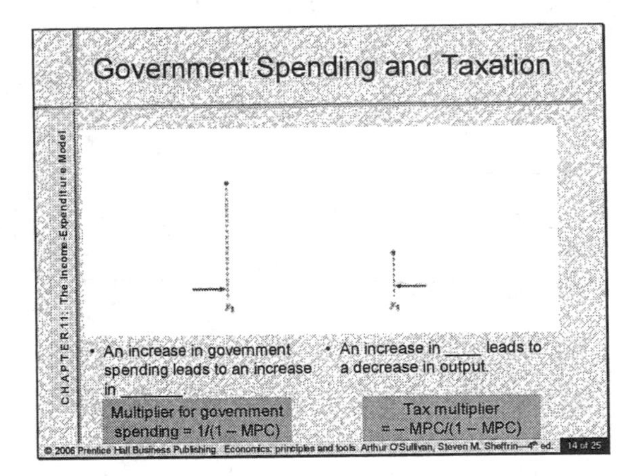

Government Spending and Taxation
CHAPTER 11: The Income-Expenditure Model
An increase in government spending leads to an increase in _______
An increase in ____ leads to a decrease in output.
Multiplier for government spending = 1/(1 – MPC)
Tax multiplier = – MPC/(1 – MPC)
© 2006 Prentice Hall Business Publishing Economics: principles and tools Arthur O'Sullivan, Steven M. Sheffrin—4th ed. 14 of 25

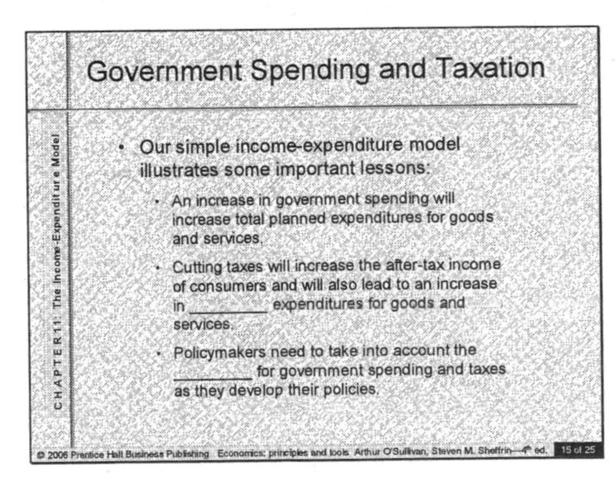

Government Spending and Taxation
CHAPTER 11: The Income-Expenditure Model
Our simple income-expenditure model illustrates some important lessons:
An increase in government spending will increase total planned expenditures for goods and services.
Cutting taxes will increase the after-tax income of consumers and will also lead to an increase in ________ expenditures for goods and services.
Policymakers need to take into account the ________ for government spending and taxes as they develop their policies.
© 2006 Prentice Hall Business Publishing Economics: principles and tools Arthur O'Sullivan, Steven M. Sheffrin—4th ed. 15 of 25

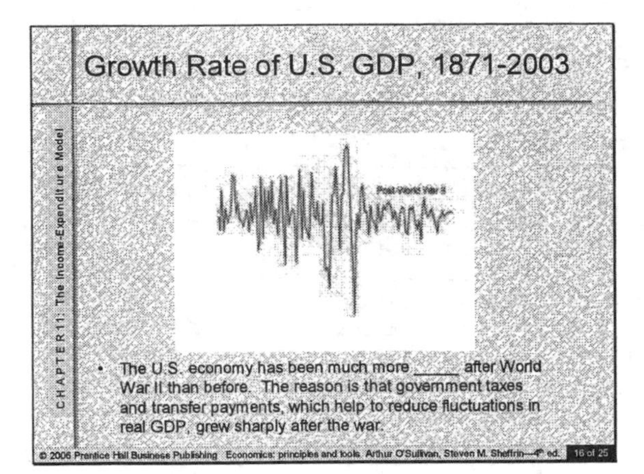
Growth Rate of U.S. GDP, 1871-2003
Post-World War II
The U.S. economy has been much more _____ after World War II than before. The reason is that government taxes and transfer payments, which help to reduce fluctuations in real GDP, grew sharply after the war.
CHAPTER 11: The Income-Expenditure Model
© 2006 Prentice Hall Business Publishing Economics: principles and tools Arthur O'Sullivan, Steven M. Sheffrin—4th ed.
16 of 25

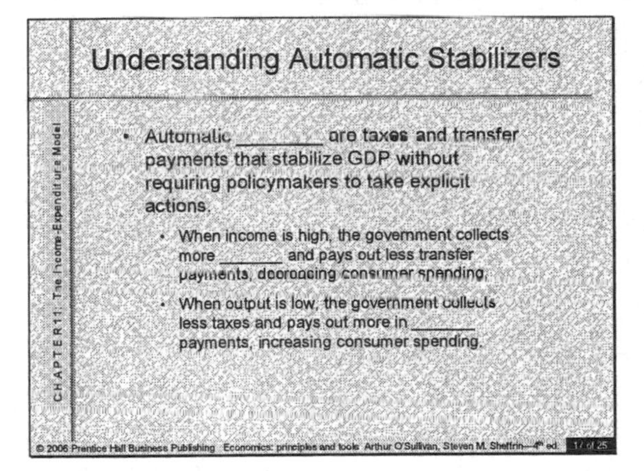
Understanding Automatic Stabilizers
Automatic ________ are taxes and transfer payments that stabilize GDP without requiring policymakers to take explicit actions.
When income is high, the government collects more _______ and pays out less transfer payments, decreasing consumer spending.
When output is low, the government collects less taxes and pays out more in _______ payments, increasing consumer spending.
CHAPTER 11: The Income-Expenditure Model
© 2006 Prentice Hall Business Publishing Economics: principles and tools Arthur O'Sullivan, Steven M. Sheffrin—4th ed.
17 of 25

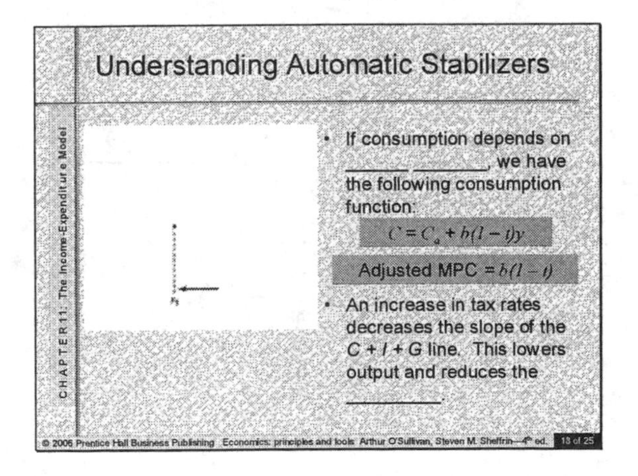
Understanding Automatic Stabilizers
If consumption depends on _______ ________, we have the following consumption function:
$C = C_a + b(1 - t)y$
Adjusted MPC $= b(1 - t)$
An increase in tax rates decreases the slope of the C + I + G line. This lowers output and reduces the _________
CHAPTER 11: The Income-Expenditure Model
© 2006 Prentice Hall Business Publishing Economics: principles and tools Arthur O'Sullivan, Steven M. Sheffrin—4th ed.
18 of 25

Understanding Automatic Stabilizers

CHAPTER 11: The Income-Expenditure Model

- In addition to automatic stabilizers, other factors that contribute to the ________ of the economy include:
  - The fact that many consumers based their spending decisions in part on their permanent income, so they will not be very _______ to changes in their current income.
  - The knowledge by firms and consumers that the federal government will often be taking actions to stabilize the economy.
  - Changes in inventory management practices. Firms have learned to make better forecasts of demand and have learned how to avoid the **inventory cycle** that resulted when _________ shocks caused additional decreases in demand.

© 2006 Prentice Hall Business Publishing Economics: principles and tools Arthur O'Sullivan, Steven M. Sheffrin—4th ed. 19 of 25

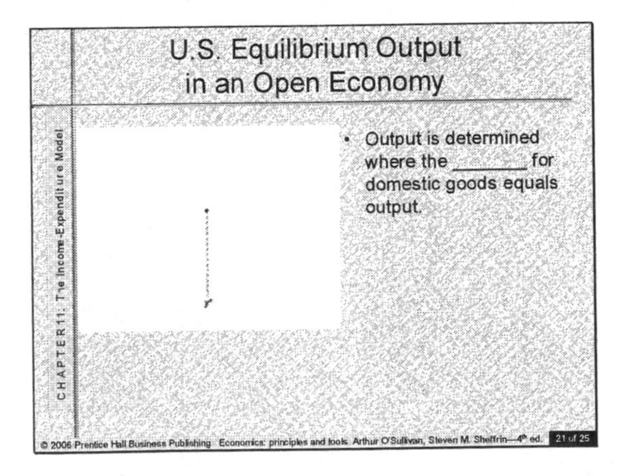

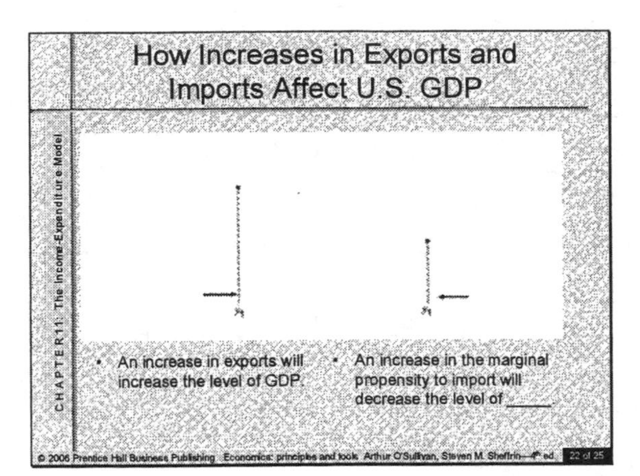
How Increases in Exports and Imports Affect U.S. GDP
CHAPTER 11: The Income-Expenditure Model
An increase in exports will increase the level of GDP.
An increase in the marginal propensity to import will decrease the level of _____.
© 2006 Prentice Hall Business Publishing Economics: principles and tools Arthur O'Sullivan, Steven M. Sheffrin—4th ed.
22 of 25

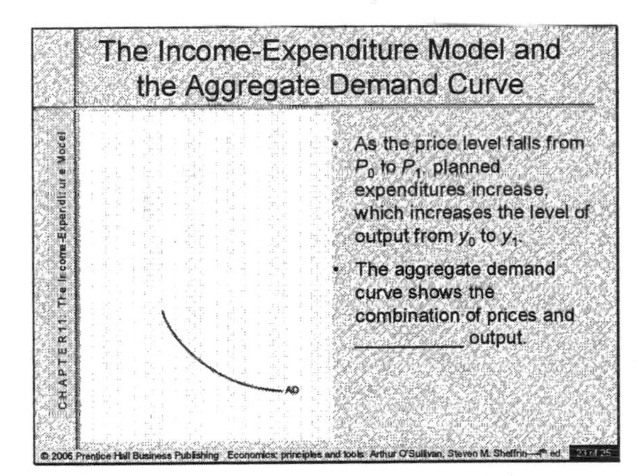
The Income-Expenditure Model and the Aggregate Demand Curve
CHAPTER 11: The Income-Expenditure Model
As the price level falls from P_0 to P_1, planned expenditures increase, which increases the level of output from y_0 to y_1.
The aggregate demand curve shows the combination of prices and __________ output.
AD
© 2006 Prentice Hall Business Publishing Economics: principles and tools Arthur O'Sullivan, Steven M. Sheffrin—4th ed.
23 of 25

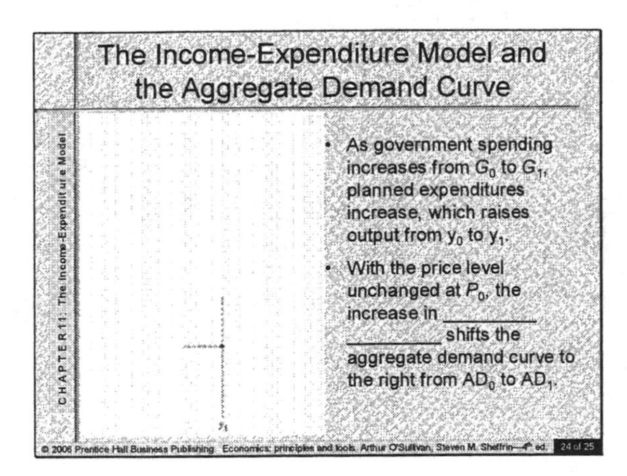
The Income-Expenditure Model and the Aggregate Demand Curve
CHAPTER 11: The Income-Expenditure Model
As government spending increases from G_0 to G_1, planned expenditures increase, which raises output from y_0 to y_1.
With the price level unchanged at P_0, the increase in ________ ________ shifts the aggregate demand curve to the right from AD_0 to AD_1.
© 2006 Prentice Hall Business Publishing Economics: principles and tools Arthur O'Sullivan, Steven M. Sheffrin—4th ed.
24 of 25

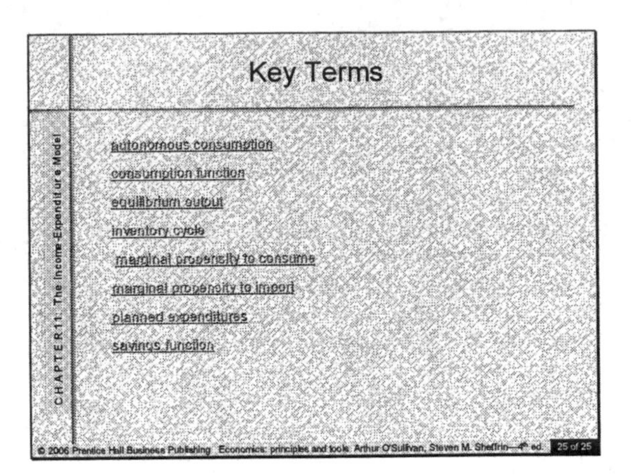
Key Terms
autonomous consumption
consumption function
equilibrium output
inventory cycle
marginal propensity to consume
marginal propensity to import
planned expenditures
savings function
CHAPTER 11: The Income-Expenditure Model
© 2006 Prentice Hall Business Publishing Economics: principles and tools Arthur O'Sullivan, Steven M. Sheffrin—4th ed.
25 of 25

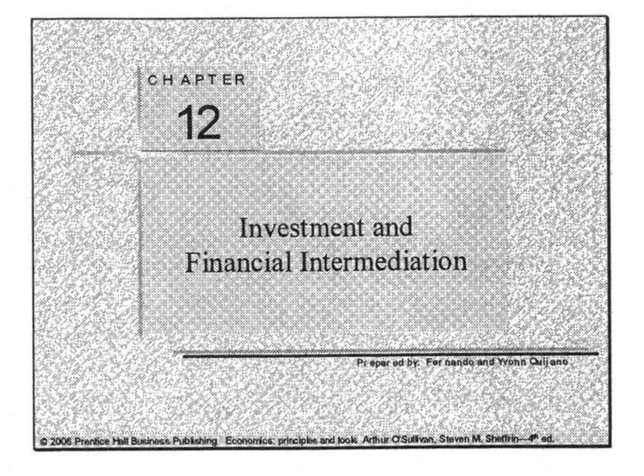

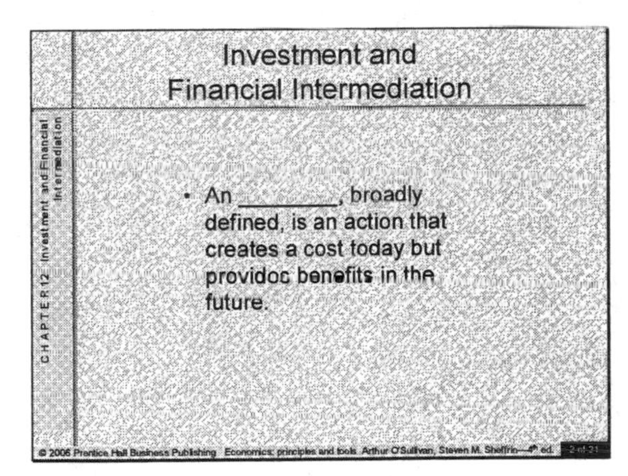

Investment: A Plunge Into the Unknown

- The ________ ______ emphasizes the role of expected growth in real GDP on investment spending.
- For example, when real GDP growth is expected to be high, firms anticipate that their investments in plant and equipment will be profitable and therefore increase their total investment spending.
- In his _______-_________ ______, Nobel laureate Paul Samuelson explained how a downturn in real GDP leads to a sharp fall in investment, which further reduces GDP through the multiplier for investment spending.

© 2006 Prentice Hall Business Publishing Economics: principles and tools Arthur O'Sullivan, Steven M. Sheffrin—4th ed. 3 of 21

Notetaker100

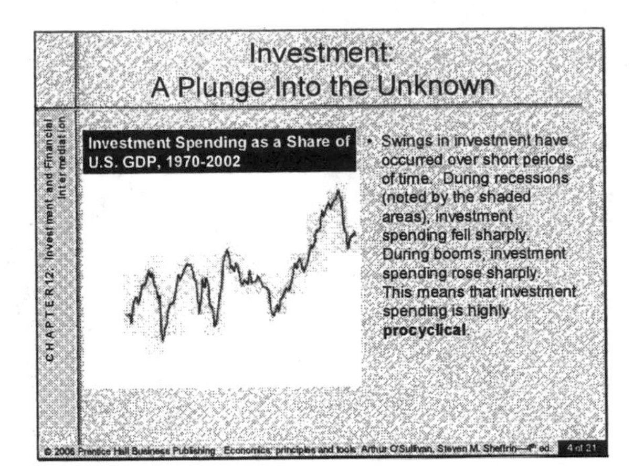

Evaluating the Future

- A dollar paid today is not the same as a dollar paid next year.
- The ______ **value** of a payment to be received in the future is the maximum amount a person is willing to pay today to get that payment later.

PRINCIPLE *of Opportunity Cost*
The opportunity cost of something is what you sacrifice to get it.

- As the interest rate increases, the opportunity cost of your funds also increases, so the present value of a given payment in the future falls. This means that you need less money today to get to your future "money goal."

© 2006 Prentice Hall Business Publishing Economics: principles and tools Arthur O'Sullivan, Steven M. Sheffrin—4th ed.

Present Value and Interest Rates

Present value = $K/(1+i)^t$

where K = amount of money you would get at some point in the future

t = amount of time, or years, in the future you're going to get the money

i = interest rate you are going to earn.

- The ______ ______ of a given payment in the future decreases as the interest rate increases. Similarly, when interest rates fall, the present value of a given payment in the future increases.

© 2006 Prentice Hall Business Publishing Economics: principles and tools Arthur O'Sullivan, Steven M. Sheffrin—4th ed.

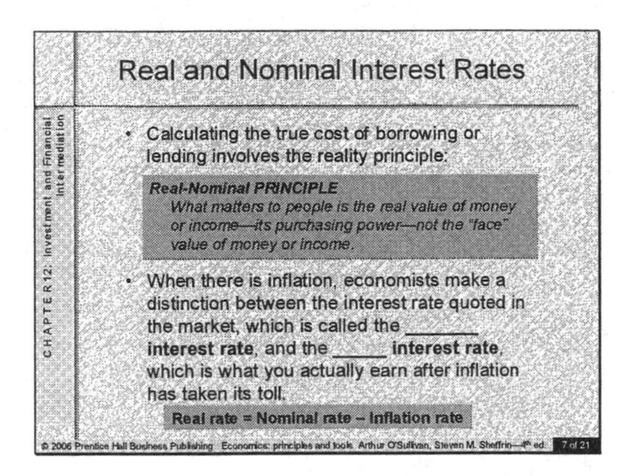

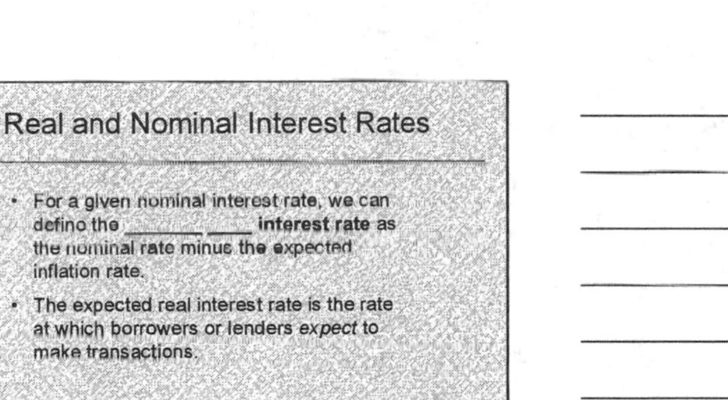

Real and Nominal Interest Rates

CHAPTER 12: Investment and Financial Intermediation

Table 26.1 Expected Real Rates of Interest for Five Countries

Country	3-Month Nominal Interest Rate	Inflation Rate Forecast for 2004	Expected Real Rate of Interest
Australia	5.5%	2.3%	2.2%
Canada	2.6	1.7	0.9
Denmark	2.3	1.6	0.7
Switzerland	0.3	0.6	-0.3
United States	1.1	1.5	-0.4

• Both nominal and expected real interest rates _____ among developed countries.

Notetaker102

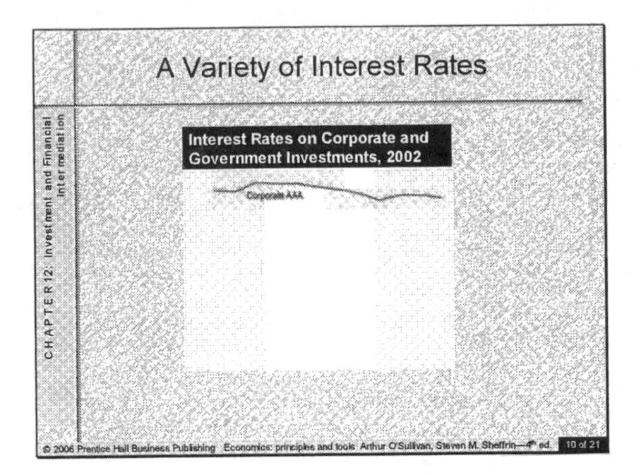

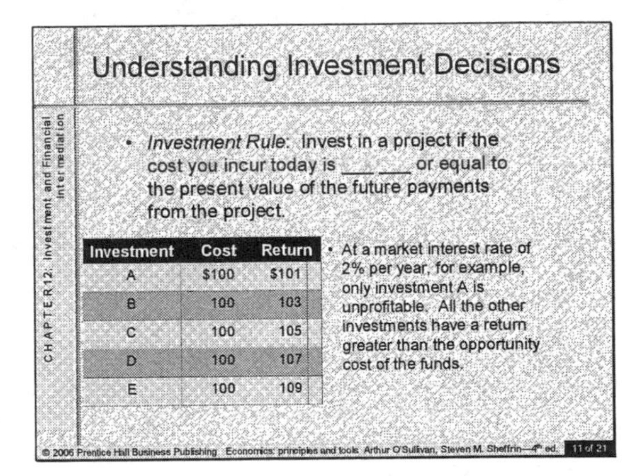

Investment	Cost	Return
A	$100	$101
B	100	103
C	100	105
D	100	107
E	100	109

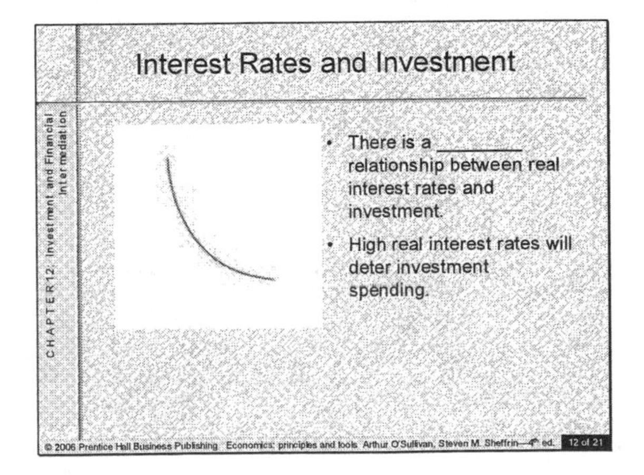

Understanding Investment Decisions

- In practice, firms need to take into account other factors besides interest rates in making their investment decisions.
- In the ____________ **theory of investment,** pioneered by Dale Jorgenson of Harvard University, taxes along with real interest rates play a key role in determining investment spending.

Investment and the Stock Market

- Economists have found that, all other things being equal, when the level of the stock market is high, investment spending also tends to be high.
- When financing a new project, a firm can:
  - Use its ______ **earnings**—the earnings the firm hasn't paid out in dividends.
  - Sell ________ **bonds** to the public.
  - Issue and sell new shares of stock.

Investment and the Stock Market

- The _-_______ __ __________, developed by Nobel laureate James Tobin of Yale University, links investment spending to stock prices. It states that investment spending increases when stock prices are high. Then, the firm uses its proceeds from the sale of stock to undertake new investment.
- Stock prices are based on the present value of the dividends people expect firms to pay in the future:

Price of stock = present value of expected future dividend payments

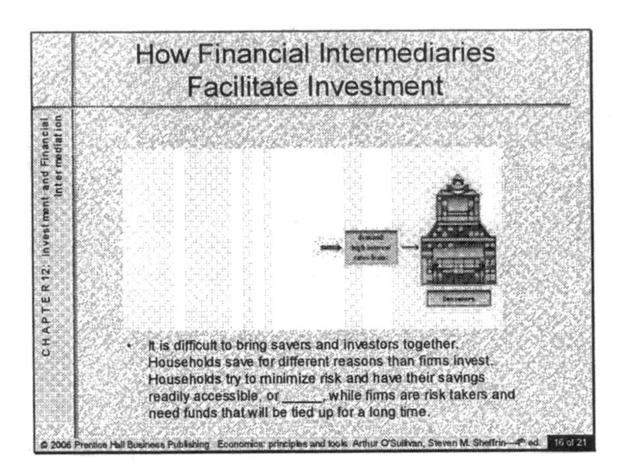
How Financial Intermediaries Facilitate Investment
CHAPTER 12: Investment and Financial Intermediation
• It is difficult to bring savers and investors together. Households save for different reasons than firms invest. Households try to minimize risk and have their savings readily accessible, or ______, while firms are risk takers and need funds that will be tied up for a long time.
© 2006 Prentice Hall Business Publishing Economics: principles and tools Arthur O'Sullivan, Steven M. Sheffrin—4th ed.
16 of 21

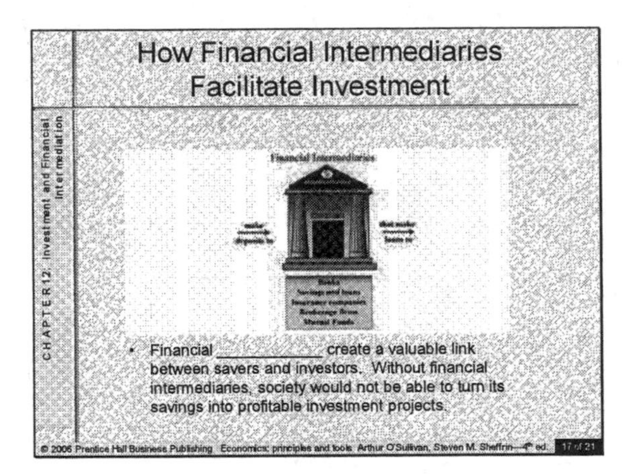
How Financial Intermediaries Facilitate Investment
CHAPTER 12: Investment and Financial Intermediation
Financial Intermediaries
• Financial ____________ create a valuable link between savers and investors. Without financial intermediaries, society would not be able to turn its savings into profitable investment projects.
© 2006 Prentice Hall Business Publishing Economics: principles and tools Arthur O'Sullivan, Steven M. Sheffrin—4th ed.
17 of 21

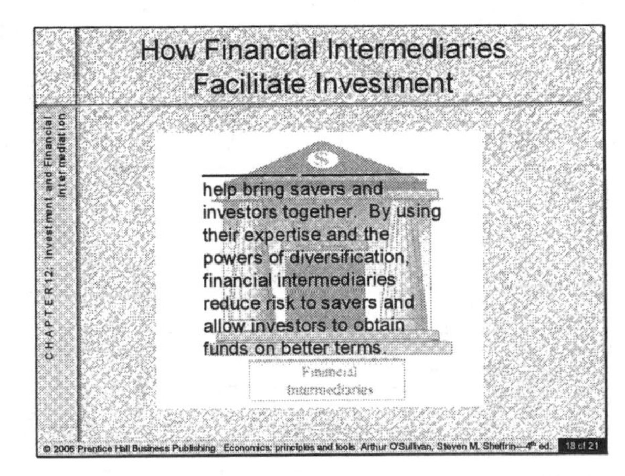
How Financial Intermediaries Facilitate Investment
CHAPTER 12: Investment and Financial Intermediation
____________ help bring savers and investors together. By using their expertise and the powers of diversification, financial intermediaries reduce risk to savers and allow investors to obtain funds on better terms.
Financial Intermediaries
© 2006 Prentice Hall Business Publishing Economics: principles and tools Arthur O'Sullivan, Steven M. Sheffrin—4th ed.
18 of 21

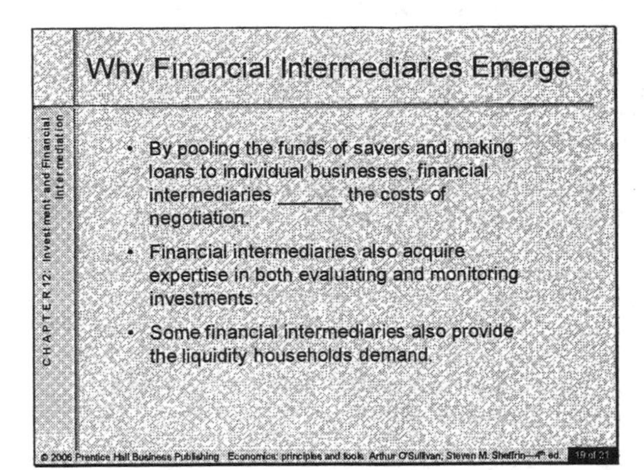

When Financial Intermediaries Malfunction

CHAPTER 12: Investment and Financial Intermediation

- In the early days of the Great Depression, many banks in the United States provided farmers or local businesses loans that turned out to be unprofitable. This worried depositors, and rumors circulated the banks would fail. Depositors panicked and tried to withdraw their money simultaneously. This is called a _____ _____.
- To prevent bank runs from happening again, in 1933 the U.S. government began providing ______ ________ on money placed in banks and savings and loans.

© 2006 Prentice Hall Business Publishing Economics: principles and tools Arthur O'Sullivan; Steven M. Sheffrin—4th ed.

Key Terms

CHAPTER 12: Investment and Financial Intermediation

accelerator theory	Neoclassical theory of investment
bank runs	nominal interest rates
corporate bond	present value
deposit insurance	procyclical
expected real interest rate	retained earnings
financial intermediaries	Q-theory of investment
liquid	real interest rate
multiplier-accelerator model	

© 2006 Prentice Hall Business Publishing Economics: principles and tools Arthur O'Sullivan; Steven M. Sheffrin—4th ed.

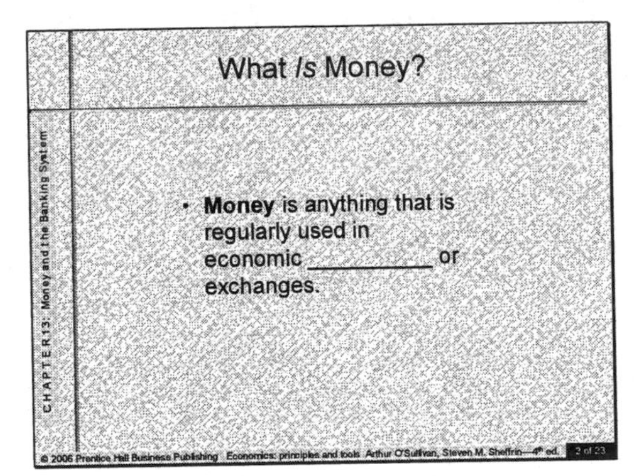

Three Properties of Money

1. Money serves as a medium of exchange:
   - A ______ **of exchange** is the property of money that exchange is made through the use of money.
   - Instead of using money, we could **barter—or** trading goods directly for goods.
   - Barter requires a _____ ________ **of wants**. The probability that one person has what the other desires is very small. Money solves that problem.

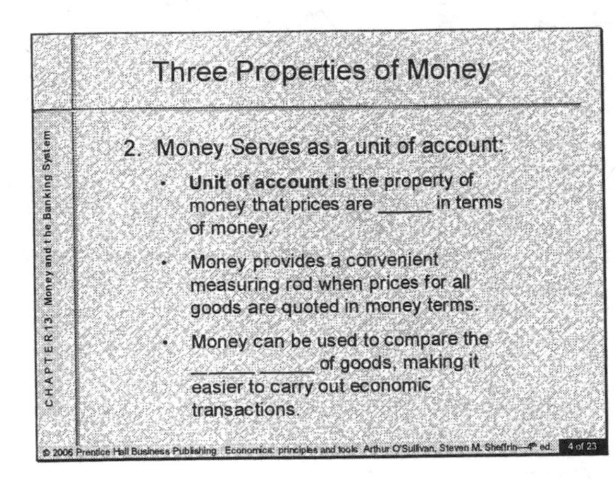

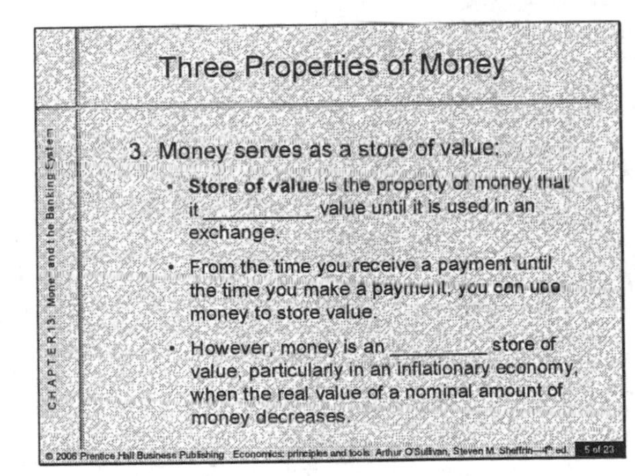

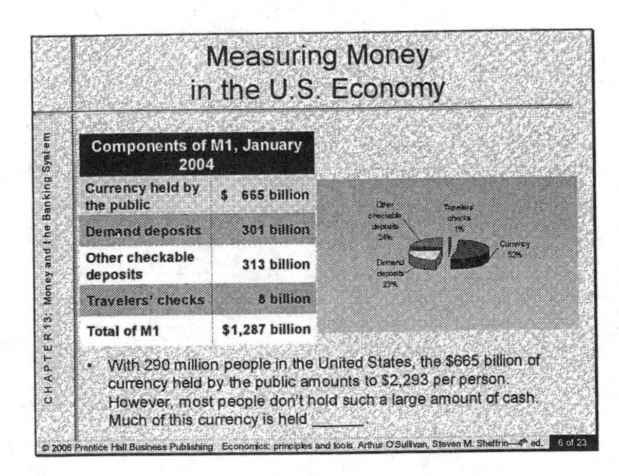

Components of M1, January 2004	
Currency held by the public	$ 665 billion
Demand deposits	301 billion
Other checkable deposits	313 billion
Travelers' checks	8 billion
Total of M1	$1,287 billion

Measuring Money in the U.S. Economy

CHAPTER 13: Money and the Banking System

- A _______ definition of money, known as M2, includes assets that can be readily turned into M1, such as deposits in money market mutual funds and savings accounts.
- While credit cards are commonly used in our economy to make transactions, they ____ ____ part of the money supply.

© 2006 Prentice Hall Business Publishing Economics: principles and tools Arthur O'Sullivan, Steven M. Sheffrin—4th ed.

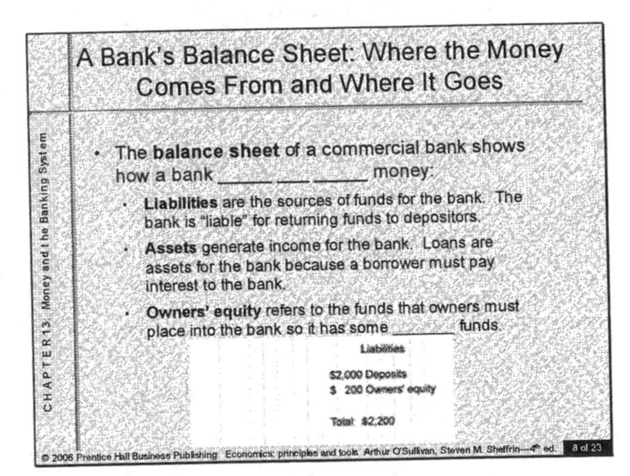

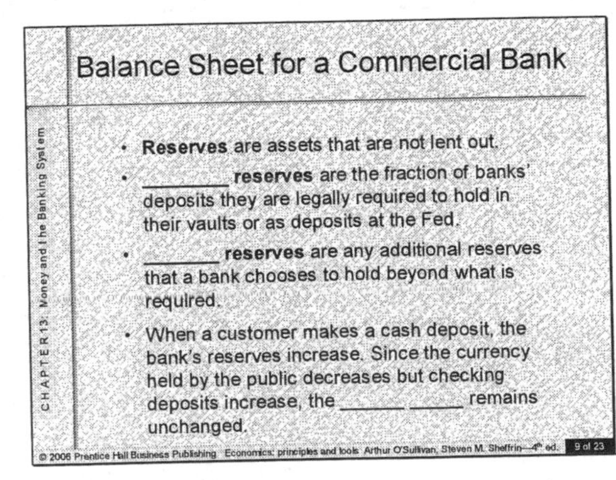

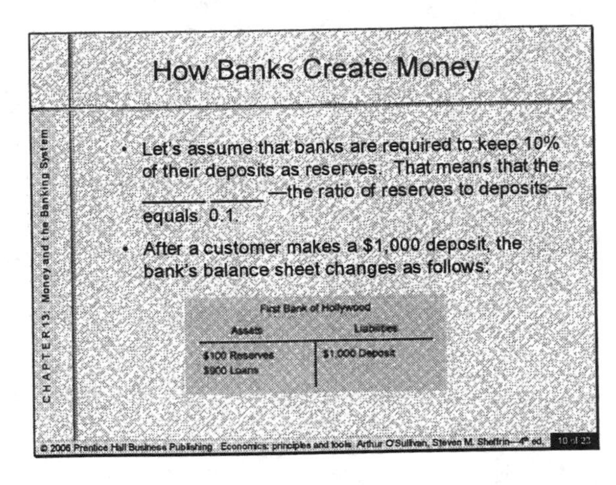
How Banks Create Money
CHAPTER 13: Money and the Banking System
Let's assume that banks are required to keep 10% of their deposits as reserves. That means that the ______ ______—the ratio of reserves to deposits—equals 0.1.
After a customer makes a $1,000 deposit, the bank's balance sheet changes as follows:
First Bank of Hollywood
Assets
Liabilities
$100 Reserves
$900 Loans
$1,000 Deposit
© 2006 Prentice Hall Business Publishing Economics: principles and tools Arthur O'Sullivan, Steven M. Sheffrin—4th ed.

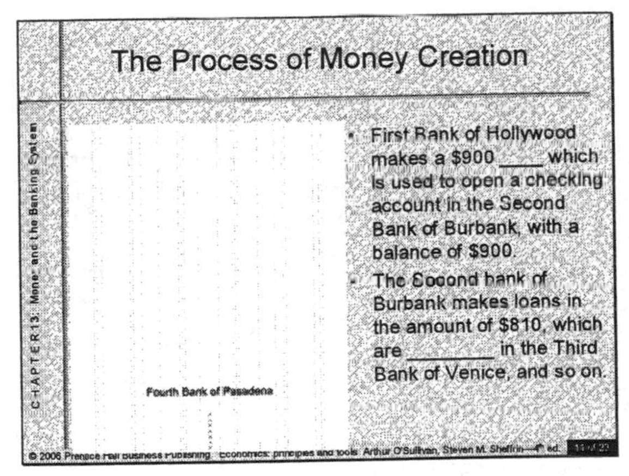
The Process of Money Creation
CHAPTER 13: Money and the Banking System
Fourth Bank of Pasadena
First Bank of Hollywood makes a $900 ____ which is used to open a checking account in the Second Bank of Burbank, with a balance of $900.
The Second bank of Burbank makes loans in the amount of $810, which are ________ in the Third Bank of Venice, and so on.
© 2006 Prentice Hall Business Publishing Economics: principles and tools Arthur O'Sullivan, Steven M. Sheffrin—4th ed.

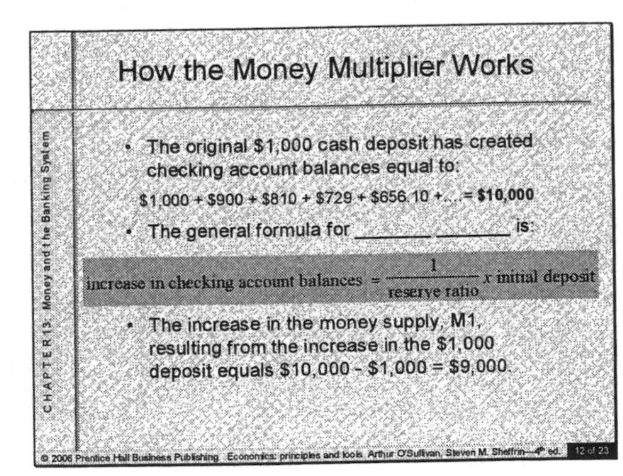
How the Money Multiplier Works
CHAPTER 13: Money and the Banking System
The original $1,000 cash deposit has created checking account balances equal to:
$1,000 + $900 + $810 + $729 + $656.10 + ... = $10,000
The general formula for ________ ________ is:
increase in checking account balances = 1 / reserve ratio x initial deposit
The increase in the money supply, M1, resulting from the increase in the $1,000 deposit equals $10,000 - $1,000 = $9,000.
© 2006 Prentice Hall Business Publishing Economics: principles and tools Arthur O'Sullivan, Steven M. Sheffrin—4th ed.
12 of 23

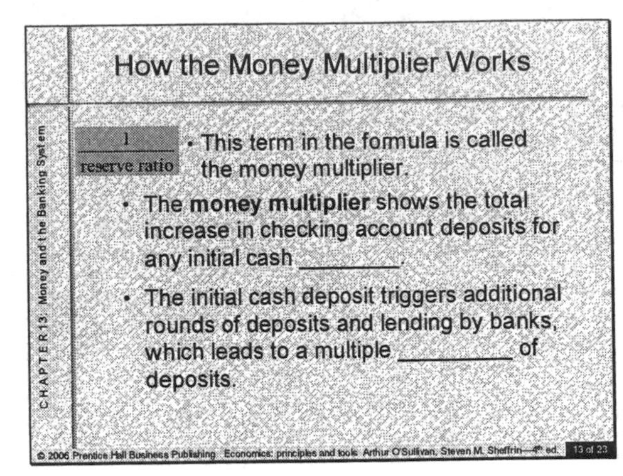

How the Money Multiplier Works

CHAPTER 13: Money and the Banking System

- The money multiplier for the United States is between 2 and 3. It is much smaller than the value in our example because, in reality, people hold part of their loans as _____. This cash is not available for the banking system to lend.

© 2006 Prentice Hall Business Publishing Economics: principles and tools Arthur O'Sullivan, Steven M. Sheffrin—4th ed.

How the Money Multiplier Works in Reverse

CHAPTER 13: Money and the Banking System

- The money multiplier also works in reverse. Assuming a reserve ratio of 10%, a _________ of $1,000 reduces reserves by $100, and results in $900 less the bank will have to lend out.
- It is important to note that when one individual writes a check to another, and the other deposits the check in the bank, the money supply will not change. Instead, the expansion in one bank's reserves will offset the _________ in the reserves of the other.

© 2006 Prentice Hall Business Publishing Economics: principles and tools Arthur O'Sullivan, Steven M. Sheffrin—4th ed.

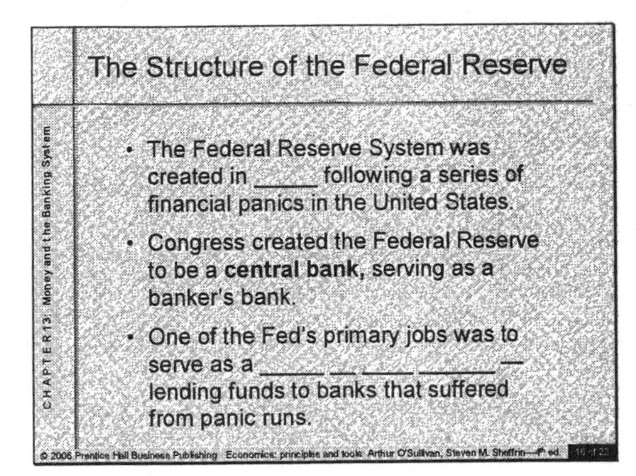

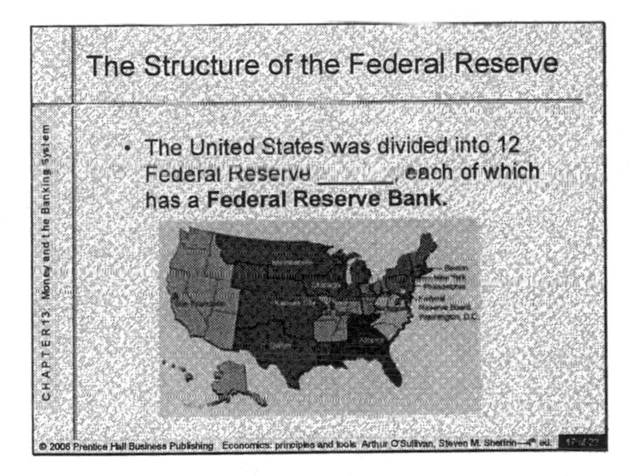

The Structure of the Federal Reserve

CHAPTER 13: Money and the Banking System

- The structure of the Federal Reserve today consists of three distinct subgroups:
  - Federal Reserve Banks
  - The ____ __ _________, and
  - The Federal Open Market Committee

© 2006 Prentice Hall Business Publishing Economics: principles and tools: Arthur O'Sullivan, Steven M. Sheffrin—4th ed.

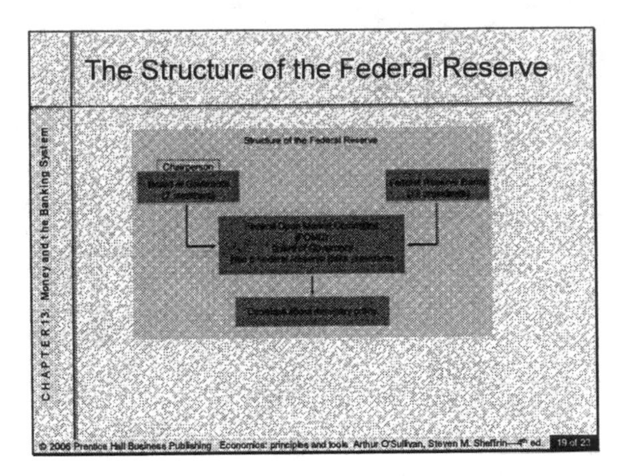

The Structure of the Federal Reserve

- The **Board of Governors of the Federal Reserve** is the true seat of power over the monetary system.
- Headquartered in Washington, DC, the _____ members of the board are appointed for staggered 14-year terms by the President and must be confirmed by the Senate.
- The chairperson serves a four-year term and is the principal spokesperson for _________ _____ in the U.S. What he speaks is carefully observed, or anticipated, by financial markets.

© 2006 Prentice Hall Business Publishing Economics: principles and tools Arthur O'Sullivan, Steven M. Sheffrin—4th ed.

The Structure of the Federal Reserve

- The **Federal Open Market Committee** (_____) is a 12-person board consisting of the seven members of the Board of Governors, the president of the New York Federal Reserve Bank, plus the presidents of four other regional Federal Reserve Banks. These four presidents serve on a rotating basis.
- The seven nonvoting bank presidents attend the meetings and provide their views. The chairperson of the Board of Governors also serves as the chairperson of the FOMC.

© 2006 Prentice Hall Business Publishing Economics: principles and tools Arthur O'Sullivan, Steven M. Sheffrin—4th ed.

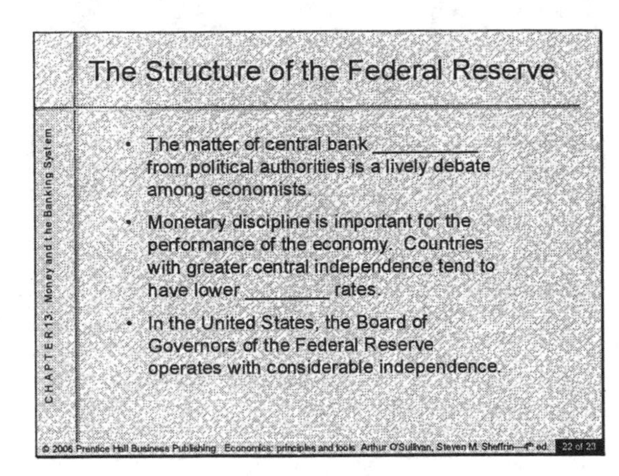
The Structure of the Federal Reserve
The matter of central bank __________ from political authorities is a lively debate among economists.
Monetary discipline is important for the performance of the economy. Countries with greater central independence tend to have lower ________ rates.
In the United States, the Board of Governors of the Federal Reserve operates with considerable independence.
CHAPTER 13: Money and the Banking System
© 2006 Prentice Hall Business Publishing Economics: principles and tools Arthur O'Sullivan, Steven M. Sheffrin—4th ed.
22 of 23

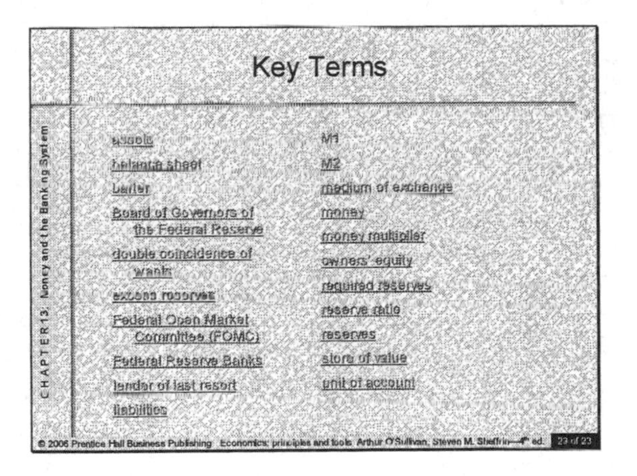
Key Terms
balance sheet
barter
Board of Governors of the Federal Reserve
double coincidence of wants
excess reserves
Federal Open Market Committee (FOMC)
Federal Reserve Banks
lender of last resort
liabilities
M1
M2
medium of exchange
money
money multiplier
owners' equity
required reserves
reserve ratio
reserves
store of value
unit of account
CHAPTER 13: Money and the Banking System
© 2006 Prentice Hall Business Publishing Economics: principles and tools Arthur O'Sullivan, Steven M. Sheffrin—4th ed.
23 of 23

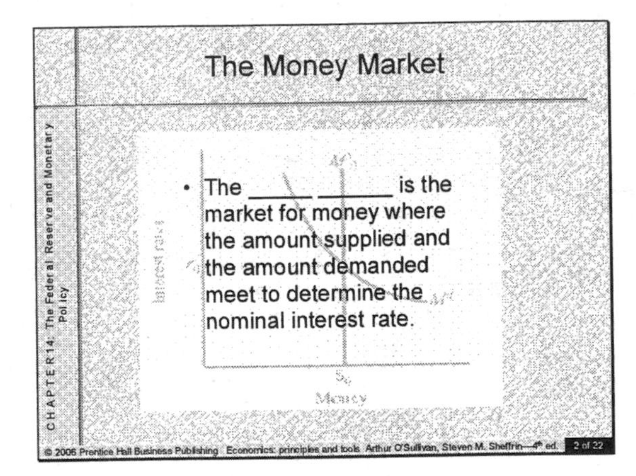

The Demand for Money

- Money is simply a part of your wealth. You can hold assets such as stocks or bonds, or you can hold wealth in the form of money.
- Holding wealth in currency or checking deposits means that you sacrifice the potential income from interest and dividends earned on stocks and bonds.
- So why hold money? Because it makes it easier to conduct transactions. Economists call this reason for holding money the ____________ **demand for money**.

CHAPTER 14: The Federal Reserve and Monetary Policy

© 2006 Prentice Hall Business Publishing Economics: principles and tools Arthur O'Sullivan, Steven M. Sheffrin—4th ed.

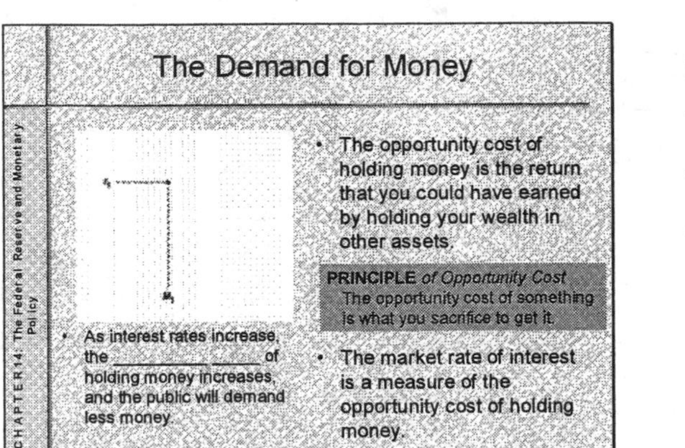
The Demand for Money
CHAPTER 14: The Federal Reserve and Monetary Policy
As interest rates increase, the ____________ of holding money increases, and the public will demand less money.
The opportunity cost of holding money is the return that you could have earned by holding your wealth in other assets.
PRINCIPLE of Opportunity Cost
The opportunity cost of something is what you sacrifice to get it.
The market rate of interest is a measure of the opportunity cost of holding money.
© 2006 Prentice Hall Business Publishing Economics: principles and tools Arthur O'Sullivan, Steven M. Sheffrin—4th ed.
4 of 22

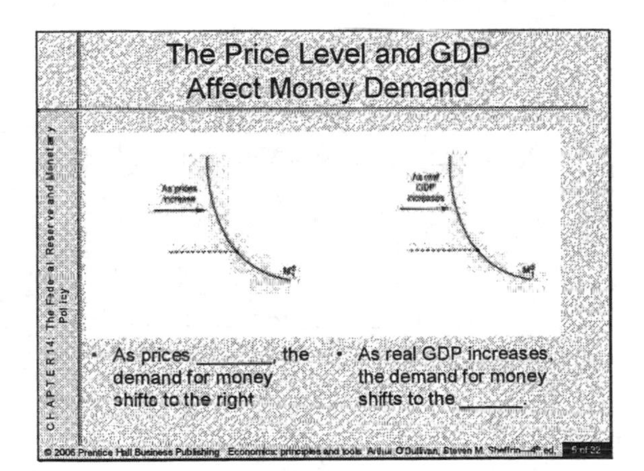
The Price Level and GDP Affect Money Demand
CHAPTER 14: The Federal Reserve and Monetary Policy
As prices increase
As real GDP increases
As prices ______, the demand for money shifts to the right
As real GDP increases, the demand for money shifts to the ______.
© 2006 Prentice Hall Business Publishing Economics: principles and tools Arthur O'Sullivan, Steven M. Sheffrin—4th ed.

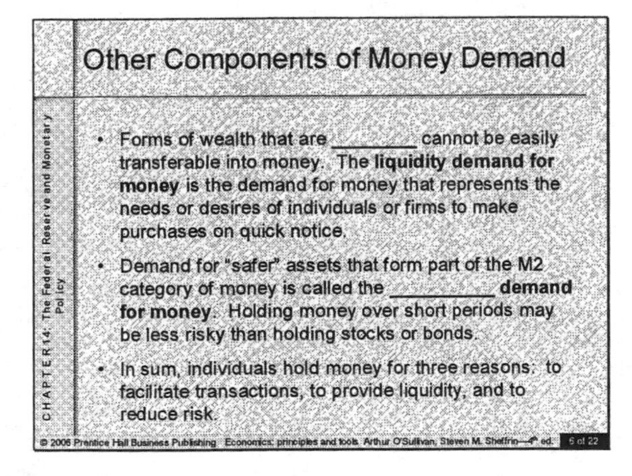
Other Components of Money Demand
CHAPTER 14: The Federal Reserve and Monetary Policy
Forms of wealth that are ________ cannot be easily transferable into money. The liquidity demand for money is the demand for money that represents the needs or desires of individuals or firms to make purchases on quick notice.
Demand for "safer" assets that form part of the M2 category of money is called the __________ demand for money. Holding money over short periods may be less risky than holding stocks or bonds.
In sum, individuals hold money for three reasons: to facilitate transactions, to provide liquidity, and to reduce risk.
© 2006 Prentice Hall Business Publishing Economics: principles and tools Arthur O'Sullivan, Steven M. Sheffrin—4th ed.
6 of 22

Notetaker116

How the Federal Reserve Can Change the Money Supply

- The Fed can increase or decrease the total amount of reserves in the banking system through either of the following operations:
  - In **open market** _________, the Federal Reserve buys bonds from the private sector.
  - In **open market** ____, the Fed's sells government bonds to the private sector.
- If the Federal Reserve wishes to increase the money supply to stimulate the economy, it buys government bonds. To decrease the money supply to slow the economy down, the Fed sells government bonds.

CHAPTER 14: The Federal Reserve and Monetary Policy

© 2006 Prentice Hall Business Publishing Economics: principles and tools Arthur O'Sullivan, Steven M. Sheffrin—4th ed.

Other Tools of Monetary Policy

- Other tools the Fed has available to change the money supply are:
  - Changing reserve requirements: banks are asked to hold a smaller or larger fraction of their deposits as reserves.
  - Changing the _______ **rate**, or the rate at which banks can borrow from the Fed.
- Before banks borrow from the Fed, they try to borrow from each other through the **federal funds market,** a market in which banks borrow and lend reserves to one another at an interest rate called the ________ ____ ____.

CHAPTER 14: The Federal Reserve and Monetary Policy

© 2006 Prentice Hall Business Publishing Economics: principles and tools Arthur O'Sullivan, Steven M. Sheffrin—4th ed.

How Interest Rates are Determined: Combining the Demand for Money with Its Supply

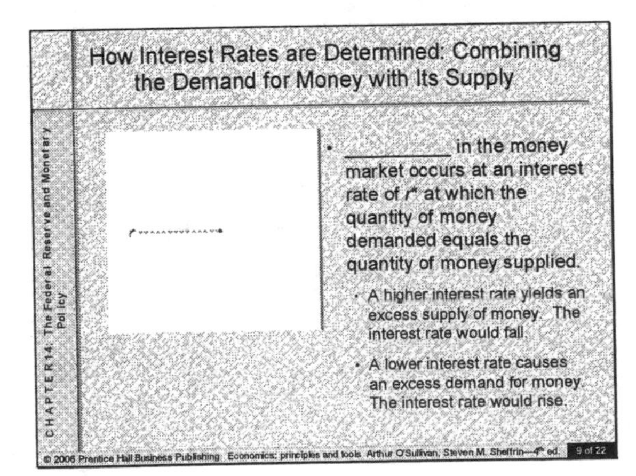

- __________ in the money market occurs at an interest rate of r^* at which the quantity of money demanded equals the quantity of money supplied.
  - A higher interest rate yields an excess supply of money. The interest rate would fall.
  - A lower interest rate causes an excess demand for money. The interest rate would rise.

CHAPTER 14: The Federal Reserve and Monetary Policy

© 2006 Prentice Hall Business Publishing Economics: principles and tools Arthur O'Sullivan, Steven M. Sheffrin—4th ed.

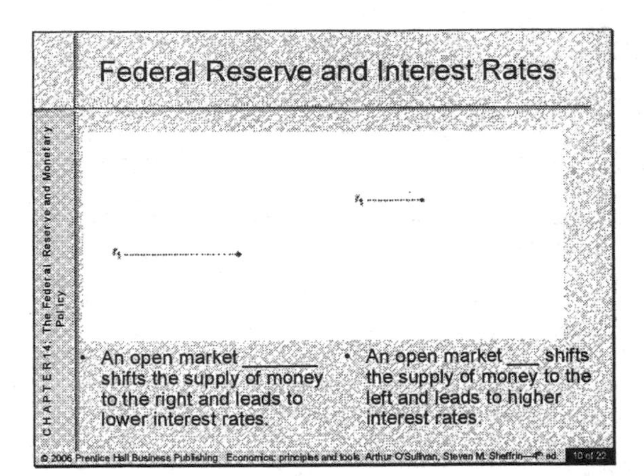
Federal Reserve and Interest Rates
CHAPTER 14: The Federal Reserve and Monetary Policy
An open market _______ shifts the supply of money to the right and leads to lower interest rates.
An open market ___ shifts the supply of money to the left and leads to higher interest rates.
© 2006 Prentice Hall Business Publishing Economics: principles and tools Arthur O'Sullivan, Steven M. Sheffrin—4th ed.
10 of 22

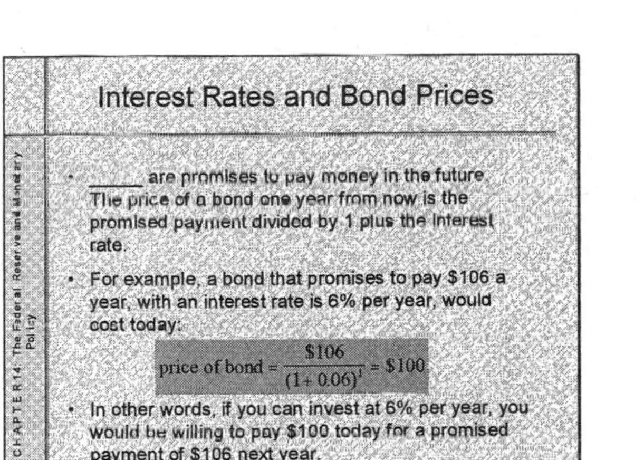
Interest Rates and Bond Prices
CHAPTER 14: The Federal Reserve and Monetary Policy
_____ are promises to pay money in the future. The price of a bond one year from now is the promised payment divided by 1 plus the interest rate.
For example, a bond that promises to pay $106 a year, with an interest rate is 6% per year, would cost today:
price of bond = $106 / (1 + 0.06)^1 = $100
In other words, if you can invest at 6% per year, you would be willing to pay $100 today for a promised payment of $106 next year.
© 2006 Prentice Hall Business Publishing Economics: principles and tools Arthur O'Sullivan, Steven M. Sheffrin—4th ed.
11 of 22

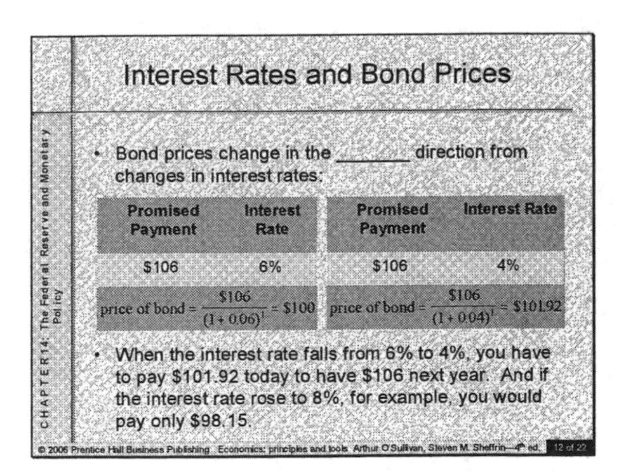
Interest Rates and Bond Prices
CHAPTER 14: The Federal Reserve and Monetary Policy
Bond prices change in the _______ direction from changes in interest rates:
Promised Payment
Interest Rate
$106
6%
price of bond = $106 / (1 + 0.06)^1 = $100
Promised Payment
Interest Rate
$106
4%
price of bond = $106 / (1 + 0.04)^1 = $101.92
When the interest rate falls from 6% to 4%, you have to pay $101.92 today to have $106 next year. And if the interest rate rose to 8%, for example, you would pay only $98.15.
© 2006 Prentice Hall Business Publishing Economics: principles and tools Arthur O'Sullivan, Steven M. Sheffrin—4th ed.
12 of 22

How Open Market Operations Directly Affect Bond Prices

- When interest rates rise, investors need ____ money to obtain the same promised payments in the future, so the price of bonds falls.
- An alternative explanation of the relationship between bond prices and interest rates deals with the supply and demand for bonds.
  - When the Fed buys bonds, in order to lower interest rates, it is increasing the demand for bonds, thus the price of bonds tends to rise.
- An ____ ________ ____ increases the supply of bonds, causing bond prices to fall and interest rates to rise.

CHAPTER 14: The Federal Reserve and Monetary Policy

© 2006 Prentice Hall Business Publishing Economics: principles and tools Arthur O'Sullivan, Steven M. Sheffrin—4th ed.

Good News for the Economy/Bad News for Bond Prices

- An increase in real ___ causes the demand for money to rise, putting upward pressure on interest rates. Consequently, bond prices will fall.
- Also, higher GDP growth leads to higher expectations of inflation which tend to push up nominal interest rates, leading to lower bond prices.
- Stock prices can also fall despite good economic news. As bond prices fall, bonds become more attractive than stocks, resulting in lower demand for stocks, and lower stock prices.

CHAPTER 14: The Federal Reserve and Monetary Policy

© 2006 Prentice Hall Business Publishing Economics: principles and tools Arthur O'Sullivan, Steven M. Sheffrin—4th ed.

Interest Rates and How They Change Investment and Output (GDP)

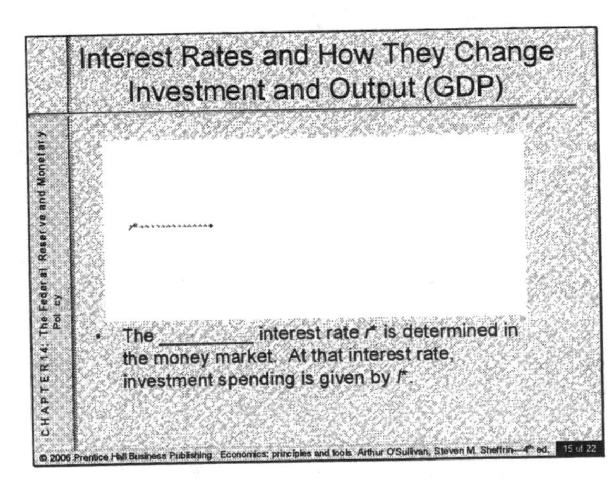

- The ________ interest rate r^* is determined in the money market. At that interest rate, investment spending is given by I^*.

CHAPTER 14: The Federal Reserve and Monetary Policy

© 2006 Prentice Hall Business Publishing Economics: principles and tools Arthur O'Sullivan, Steven M. Sheffrin—4th ed.

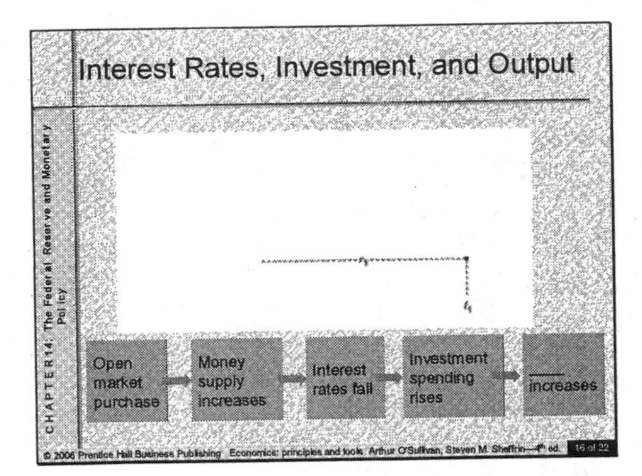
Interest Rates, Investment, and Output
CHAPTER 14: The Federal Reserve and Monetary Policy
Open market purchase
Money supply increases
Interest rates fall
Investment spending rises
____ increases
© 2006 Prentice Hall Business Publishing Economics: principles and tools Arthur O'Sullivan, Steven M. Sheffrin—4th ed.
16 of 22

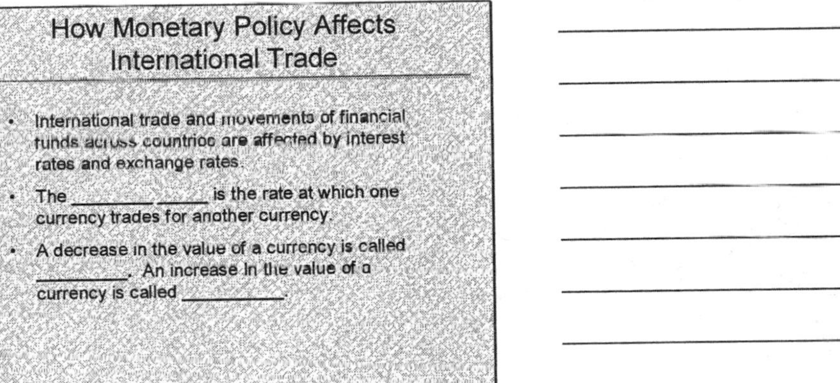
How Monetary Policy Affects International Trade
CHAPTER 14: The Federal Reserve and Monetary Policy
• International trade and movements of financial funds across countries are affected by interest rates and exchange rates.
• The ________ _____ is the rate at which one currency trades for another currency.
• A decrease in the value of a currency is called ________. An increase in the value of a currency is called ________.
© 2006 Prentice Hall Business Publishing Economics: principles and tools Arthur O'Sullivan, Steven M. Sheffrin—4th ed.
17 of 22

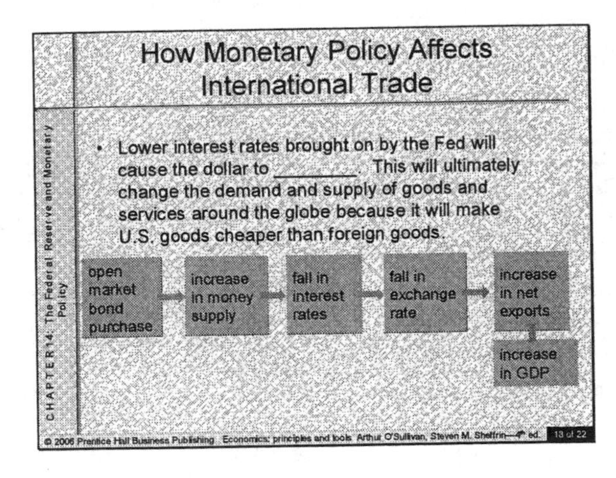
How Monetary Policy Affects International Trade
CHAPTER 14: The Federal Reserve and Monetary Policy
• Lower interest rates brought on by the Fed will cause the dollar to ________. This will ultimately change the demand and supply of goods and services around the globe because it will make U.S. goods cheaper than foreign goods.
open market bond purchase
increase in money supply
fall in interest rates
fall in exchange rate
increase in net exports
increase in GDP
© 2006 Prentice Hall Business Publishing Economics: principles and tools Arthur O'Sullivan, Steven M. Sheffrin—4th ed.
18 of 22

Notetaker120

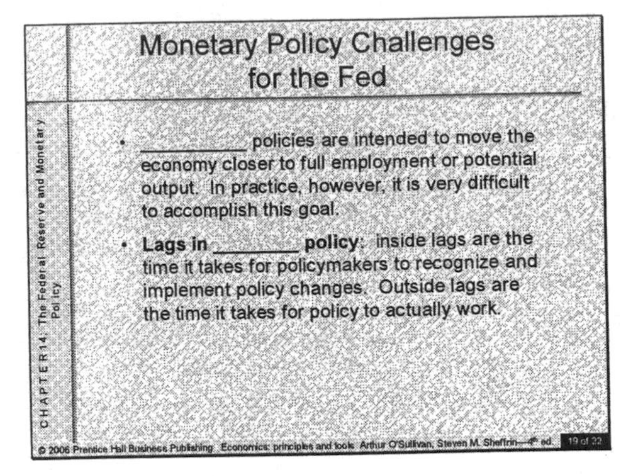

Monetary Policy Challenges for the Fed

- Inside lags are relatively short, while outside lags are quite long.
- Because of the long outside lags and difficulties in forecasting the economy, many economists believe that the Fed should not take a very active role in trying to stabilize the economy. Instead, they recommend that the Fed concentrate on keeping the inflation rate _____ ___ ______.

CHAPTER 14: The Federal Reserve and Monetary Policy

© 2006 Prentice Hall Business Publishing Economics: principles and tools Arthur O'Sullivan, Steven M. Sheffrin—4th ed.

Influencing Market Expectations: From the Federal Funds Rate to Interest Rates on Long-Term Bonds

- The Fed only directly controls very short term interest rates in the economy, not long-term interest rates.
- However, ____-___ investment decisions by firms and households are typically based on long-term interest rates. So for the Fed to control spending it must somehow influence long-term rates.
- The Fed can influence long-term rates by influencing short-term interest rates because long-term interest rates are an average of the current short-term interest rate and expected future short-term rates.

CHAPTER 14: The Federal Reserve and Monetary Policy

© 2006 Prentice Hall Business Publishing Economics: principles and tools Arthur O'Sullivan, Steven M. Sheffrin—4th ed.

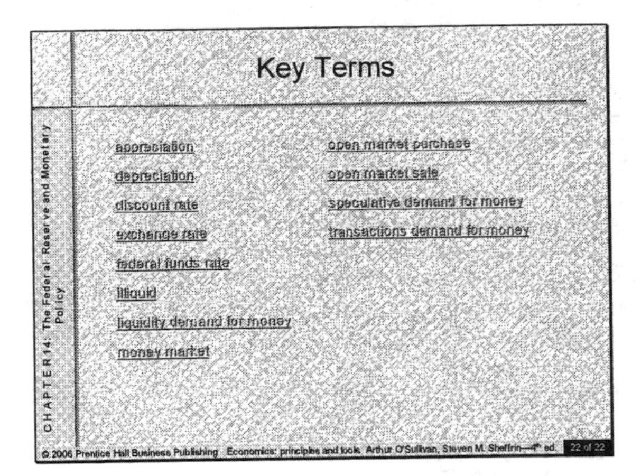
Key Terms
appreciation
depreciation
discount rate
exchange rate
federal funds rate
illiquid
liquidity demand for money
money market
open market purchase
open market sale
speculative demand for money
transactions demand for money
CHAPTER 14: The Federal Reserve and Monetary Policy
© 2006 Prentice Hall Business Publishing Economics: principles and tools Arthur O'Sullivan, Steven M. Sheffrin—4th ed.
22 of 22

The Difference Between the Short and Long Run

- In the short run:
  - Wages and prices are ______. Short-run, analysis applies to the period of time when wages and prices do not change—at least not substantially.
  - The level of ____ is determined by the current demand for goods and services.
  - Monetary and fiscal ________ can have an impact on demand and GDP.

© 2006 Prentice Hall Business Publishing Economics: principles and tools Arthur O'Sullivan, Steven M. Sheffrin—4th ed.

The Difference Between the Short and Long Run

- In the long run:
  - Prices are flexible.
  - The level of GDP is determined by the demand and supply for labor, the stock of capital, and technological progress. The economy operates at _____ __________.
  - Output can't be increased by changes in demand. Any increases in government spending must come at the ________ of some other use of output. An increase in the money supply will only cause the price level to rise.

© 2006 Prentice Hall Business Publishing Economics: principles and tools Arthur O'Sullivan, Steven M. Sheffrin—4th ed.

Wage and Prices and Their Adjustment Over Time

- Wages and prices change everyday. Sometimes, we see them rising and falling together.
- As prices rise, workers need higher nominal wages to maintain their _____ _____. This is an illustration of the reality principle:

> ***Real-Nominal PRINCIPLE***
> *What matters to people is the real value of money or income—its purchasing power—not the "face" value of money or income.*

- This process by which rising wages cause higher prices and higher prices feed higher wages in known as the _________ _______.

© 2006 Prentice Hall Business Publishing Economics: principles and tools Arthur O'Sullivan, Steven M. Sheffrin—4th ed.

The Wage-price Spiral

- A wage-price spiral occurs when actual output produced exceeds the ________ output of the economy. When the economy is producing below full employment or potential output, the process works in reverse.

Table 29.1 Unemployment, Output, and Wage and Price Changes

When unemployment is below the natural rate. . .	*When unemployment is above the natural rate. . .*
Output is above potential. Wages and prices rise.	Output is below potential. Wages and prices fall.

© 2006 Prentice Hall Business Publishing Economics: principles and tools Arthur O'Sullivan, Steven M. Sheffrin—4th ed.

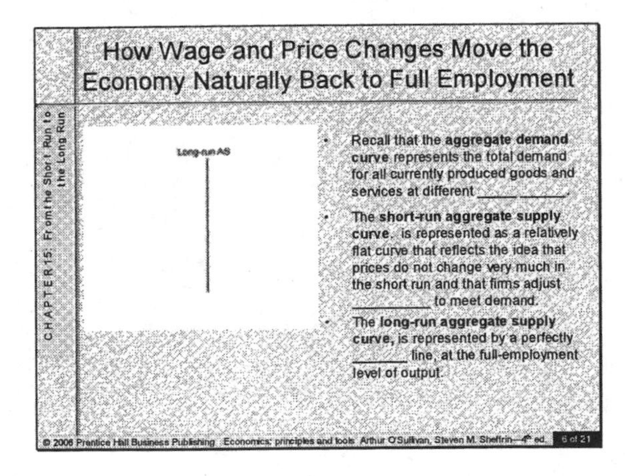

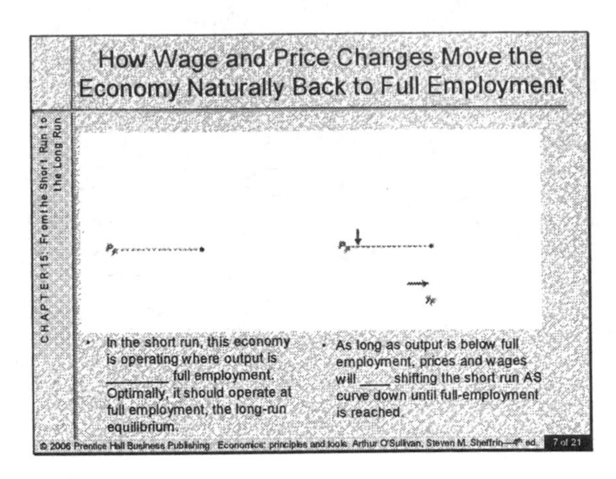
How Wage and Price Changes Move the Economy Naturally Back to Full Employment
CHAPTER 15: From the Short Run to the Long Run
In the short run, this economy is operating where output is ________ full employment. Optimally, it should operate at full employment, the long-run equilibrium.
As long as output is below full employment, prices and wages will ____ shifting the short run AS curve down until full-employment is reached.
© 2006 Prentice Hall Business Publishing Economics: principles and tools Arthur O'Sullivan, Steven M. Sheffrin—4th ed.
7 of 21

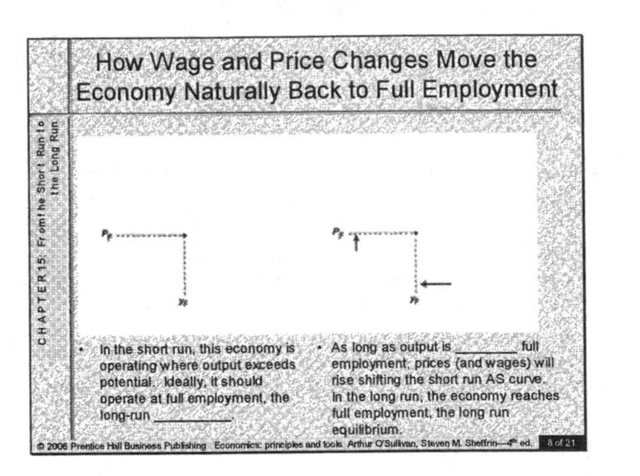
How Wage and Price Changes Move the Economy Naturally Back to Full Employment
CHAPTER 15: From the Short Run to the Long Run
In the short run, this economy is operating where output exceeds potential. Ideally, it should operate at full employment, the long-run ________
As long as output is ________ full employment, prices (and wages) will rise shifting the short run AS curve. In the long run, the economy reaches full employment, the long run equilibrium.
© 2006 Prentice Hall Business Publishing Economics: principles and tools Arthur O'Sullivan, Steven M. Sheffrin—4th ed.
8 of 21

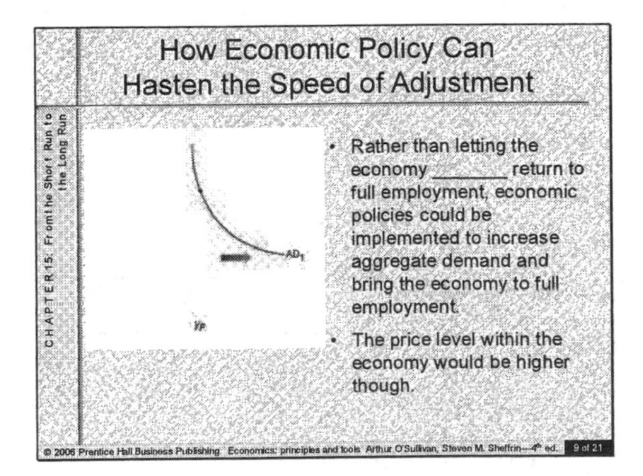
How Economic Policy Can Hasten the Speed of Adjustment
CHAPTER 15: From the Short Run to the Long Run
AD1
Rather than letting the economy ________ return to full employment, economic policies could be implemented to increase aggregate demand and bring the economy to full employment.
The price level within the economy would be higher though.
© 2006 Prentice Hall Business Publishing Economics: principles and tools Arthur O'Sullivan, Steven M. Sheffrin—4th ed.
9 of 21

Liquidity Traps

CHAPTER 15: From the Short Run to the Long Run

- Keynes expressed doubts about whether a country could recover from a major recession without ______ policy. He had two distinct reasons:
  - First, the adjustment process requires interest rates to fall, but if ______ ______ ______ become so low that they cannot fall any further, the economy has fallen into what Keynes called a **liquidity trap**, and the adjustment process no longer works.
  - Second, Keynes also feared that falling prices could hurt businesses.

© 2006 Prentice Hall Business Publishing Economics: principles and tools Arthur O'Sullivan, Steven M. Sheffrin—4th ed. 10 of 21

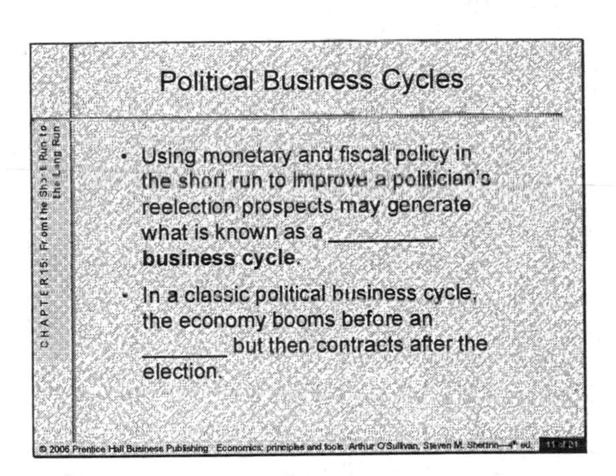

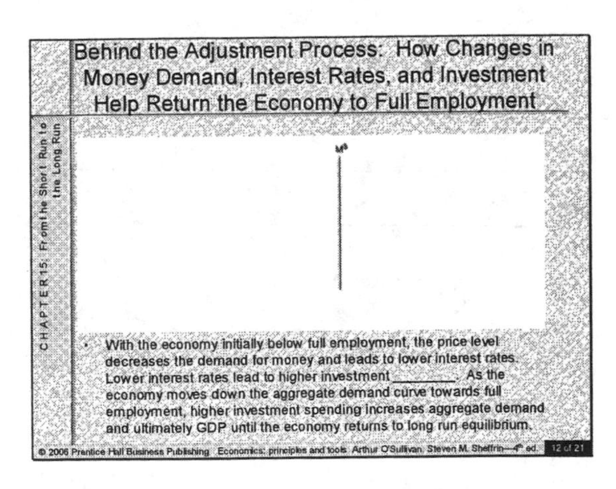

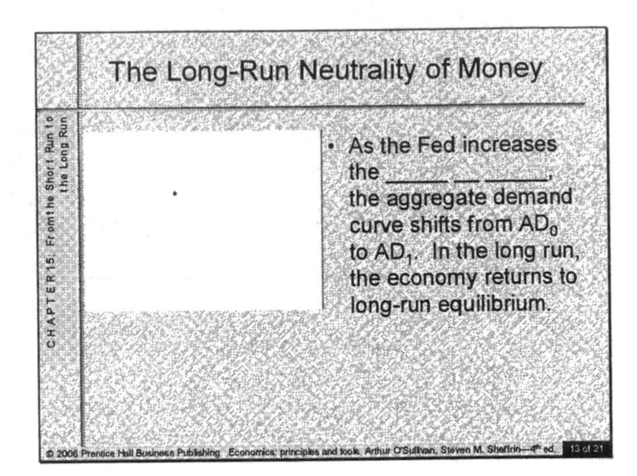
The Long-Run Neutrality of Money
CHAPTER 15: From the Short Run to the Long Run
• As the Fed increases the ______ __ ______, the aggregate demand curve shifts from AD0 to AD1. In the long run, the economy returns to long-run equilibrium.
© 2006 Prentice Hall Business Publishing Economics: principles and tools Arthur O'Sullivan, Steven M. Sheffrin—4th ed.
13 of 21

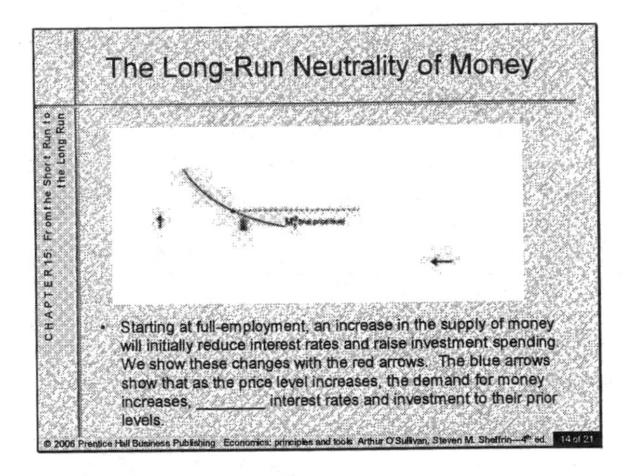
The Long-Run Neutrality of Money
CHAPTER 15: From the Short Run to the Long Run
• Starting at full-employment, an increase in the supply of money will initially reduce interest rates and raise investment spending. We show these changes with the red arrows. The blue arrows show that as the price level increases, the demand for money increases, ______ interest rates and investment to their prior levels.
© 2006 Prentice Hall Business Publishing Economics: principles and tools Arthur O'Sullivan, Steven M. Sheffrin—4th ed.
14 of 21

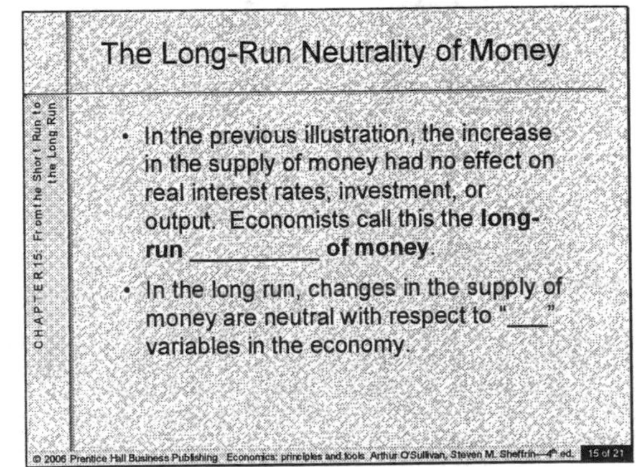
The Long-Run Neutrality of Money
CHAPTER 15: From the Short Run to the Long Run
• In the previous illustration, the increase in the supply of money had no effect on real interest rates, investment, or output. Economists call this the long-run __________ of money.
• In the long run, changes in the supply of money are neutral with respect to "___" variables in the economy.
© 2006 Prentice Hall Business Publishing Economics: principles and tools Arthur O'Sullivan, Steven M. Sheffrin—4th ed.
15 of 21

Crowding Out in the Long Run

- Starting at full employment, an increase in government spending raises output above ______________. As wages and prices increase, the demand for money increases, raising interest rates and reducing investment. The economy returns to full employment but with a higher level of interest rates and a lower level of investment spending.

© 2006 Prentice Hall Business Publishing Economics: principles and tools Arthur O'Sullivan, Steven M. Sheffrin—4th ed.

Crowding Out in the Long Run

- In the previous illustration, a long run increase in government spending has no long-run effect on the level of output—just the interest rate. Instead, the increase in government spending _________, or **crowded out**, private investment spending.

© 2006 Prentice Hall Business Publishing Economics: principles and tools Arthur O'Sullivan, Steven M. Sheffrin—4th ed.

"Classical Economics" in Historical Perspective

- Classical economics refers to the body of work developed over time starting with ______ ______ in the late eighteenth and nineteenth century.
- The term "______ ______" was first used by Keynes to contrast his "Keynesian" or activist model with the conventional economic wisdom of the time that didn't emphasize the difficulties that the economy could face in the short run.

© 2006 Prentice Hall Business Publishing Economics: principles and tools Arthur O'Sullivan, Steven M. Sheffrin—4th ed.

Say's Law

- Say's law is the ________ that "supply creates its own demand." Since production creates an equivalent amount of income, there could never be a shortage of demand for total goods and services in the economy nor any excess. If consumers saved, those savings would eventually turn into investment spending.
- Keynes argued that there could be situations in which total demand fell short of total production in the economy, leading to a recession or ________.

© 2006 Prentice Hall Business Publishing Economics: principles and tools Arthur O'Sullivan, Steven M. Sheffrin—4th ed.

Keynesian and Classical Debates

- In the 1940s, professors Don ________ and Nobel laureate Franco Modigliani clarified the conditions for which the classical model would hold true.
- They emphasized that one of the necessary conditions was that wages and prices be fully ________—that is, that they adjust rapidly to changes in demand and supply.

© 2006 Prentice Hall Business Publishing Economics: principles and tools Arthur O'Sullivan, Steven M. Sheffrin—4th ed.

Key Terms

aggregate demand curve
crowding out
liquidity trap
long-run aggregate supply curve
long-run neutrality of money
political business cycle
short run aggregate supply curve
wage-price spiral

© 2006 Prentice Hall Business Publishing Economics: principles and tools Arthur O'Sullivan, Steven M. Sheffrin—4th ed.

Money Growth, Inflation and Interest Rates

- An economy can, in principle, produce at full employment with any ________ rate.
- As we have seen, in the long run, money is neutral. If the Federal Reserve increases the money supply at 5% a year, there will be 5% annual inflation.

CHAPTER 16 The Dynamics of Inflation and Unemployment

© 2006 Prentice Hall Business Publishing Economics: principles and tools Arthur O'Sullivan, Steven M. Sheffrin—4th ed.

Inflation in a Steady State

- The ______ **wages**—wages in dollars—of workers are all rising at 5% a year. However, because prices are also rising at 5% a year, ____ **wages**—wages adjusted for changes in purchasing power—remain constant.
- Some workers might believe that their nominal wage increases are real wage increases. These workers suffer from what economists call _______ ________, a confusion of real and nominal magnitudes.

CHAPTER 16 The Dynamics of Inflation and Unemployment

© 2006 Prentice Hall Business Publishing Economics: principles and tools Arthur O'Sullivan, Steven M. Sheffrin—4th ed.

Inflation in a Steady State

- After a time, everyone in the economy would begin to expect that the 5% annual inflation that had occurred in the past would continue in the future. Economists call this ____________ **of inflation.**
- Continued inflation becomes the normal state of affairs, and people "build it into" their daily decision-making process.

Inflation Expectations and Interest Rates

- When the public expects inflation, real and nominal rates of interest will differ.

Nominal rate of interest = **Real rate of interest** + **Expected rate of inflation**

- In the long run, the ____ rate of interest does not depend on monetary policy because money is neutral. However, ______ rates of interest do depend on monetary policy because monetary policy affects the rate of inflation, which in the long run is determined by the growth of the money supply.

Inflation Expectations and Money Demand

- If the public expects 5% inflation a year, then its demand for money will also increase by 5% a year.

_____-_______ PRINCIPLE

What matters to people is the real value of money or income—its purchasing power—not the "face" value of money or income.

- As long as the Fed allows the supply of money to increase by 5%–the same amount as inflation—the demand for money and its supply will both grow at the same rate, then real interest rates and nominal interest rates will not change.

How Changes in the Growth Rate of Money Affect the Steady State

CHAPTER 16: The Dynamics of Inflation and Unemployment

- If money demand grows at 5% but the money supply grows at only 4%, there will be an increase in both real and nominal interest rates. The reduction in the money supply is contractionary.
- In the long run, _______ interest rates will be 1% lower since inflation has fallen, and nominal rates reflect expectations of ongoing inflation.
- In the short run, a policy of tight money leads to slower money growth, higher interest rates, and lower output. But in the long run, reduced money growth results in lower interest rates, lower inflation, and no effect on the level of output.

© 2006 Prentice Hall Business Publishing Economics: principles and tools Arthur O'Sullivan, Steven M. Sheffrin—4th ed.

Understanding the Expectations Phillips Curve: The Relationship Between Unemployment and Inflation

CHAPTER 16: The Dynamics of Inflation and Unemployment

- The relationship between unemployment and inflation when there are expectations about inflation is known as the **expectations _______ curve**.
- The expectations Phillips curve involves the notion that unemployment varies with __________ ________.

© 2006 Prentice Hall Business Publishing Economics: principles and tools Arthur O'Sullivan, Steven M. Sheffrin—4th ed.

Understanding the Expectations Phillips Curve: The Relationship Between Unemployment and Inflation

CHAPTER 16: The Dynamics of Inflation and Unemployment

- With higher perceived real wages being offered, potential workers will be inclined to accept the jobs offered them. After workers recognize that the inflation rate is higher, they will no longer confuse the higher _______ wages with higher _____ wages, and unemployment will return to its natural rate.

Table 30.1 Expectations and Business Fluctuations

	Unemployment	Inflation
Boom	Unemployment below the natural rate	Inflation higher than expected
Recession	Unemployment above the natural rate	Inflation lower than expected

© 2006 Prentice Hall Business Publishing Economics: principles and tools Arthur O'Sullivan, Steven M. Sheffrin—4th ed.

Are the Public's Expectations About Inflation Rational?

CHAPTER 16: The Dynamics of Inflation and Unemployment

- There are two broad classes of theories of how the public forms its expectations:
  - Some economists and psychologists, including Nobel laureate Herbert Simon, believe that the public uses simple rules-of-thumb to predict future inflation.
  - An alternative view, called the theory of ________ ________, holds that workers and firms base their expectations on all available information.

© 2006 Prentice Hall Business Publishing Economics: principles and tools Arthur O'Sullivan, Steven M. Sheffrin—4th ed.

U.S. Inflation and Unemployment in the 1980s

CHAPTER 16: The Dynamics of Inflation and Unemployment

- In the early 1980s, high real interest rates eventually caused the unemployment rate to rise to over 10% by 1983.
- As the actual unemployment exceeded the natural rate of unemployment, the inflation rate fell, just as was predicted by the ________ ______ _____. The severe recession had done its job in reducing the inflation rate.

© 2006 Prentice Hall Business Publishing Economics: principles and tools Arthur O'Sullivan, Steven M. Sheffrin—4th ed.

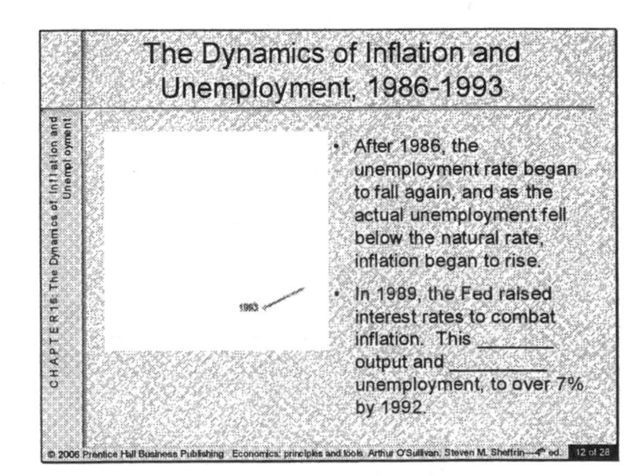

Shifts in the Natural Rate of Unemployment

CHAPTER 16: The Dynamics of Inflation and Unemployment

- The _______ ____ of unemployment can shift over time. The factors that cause this include:
  - Demographics, and the composition of the workforce.
  - Institutional changes, or changes in laws and regulations that affect unemployment benefits and restrictions placed on employers that make it difficult to fire workers.

© 2006 Prentice Hall Business Publishing Economics: principles and tools Arthur O'Sullivan, Steven M. Sheffrin—4th ed.

Shifts in the Natural Rate of Unemployment

CHAPTER 16: The Dynamics of Inflation and Unemployment

- The natural rate of unemployment can shift over time. The factors that cause this include:
  - The state of the economy. During _________ workers lose some of their skills, which could lead to longer-term unemployment.
  - Changes in the growth of labor productivity. Unexpected productivity growth may be inconsistent with workers' asking wages.

© 2006 Prentice Hall Business Publishing Economics: principles and tools Arthur O'Sullivan, Steven M. Sheffrin—4th ed.

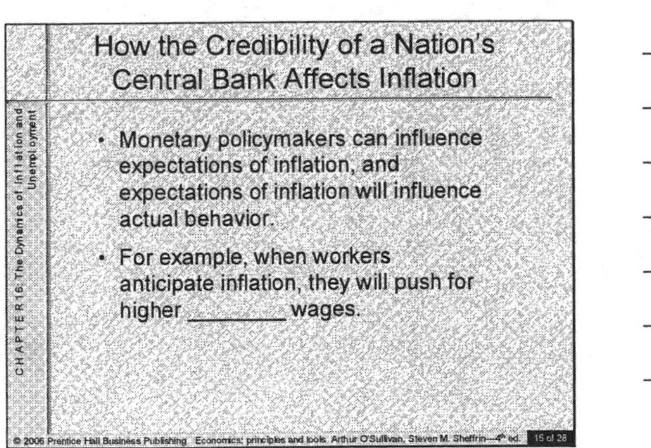

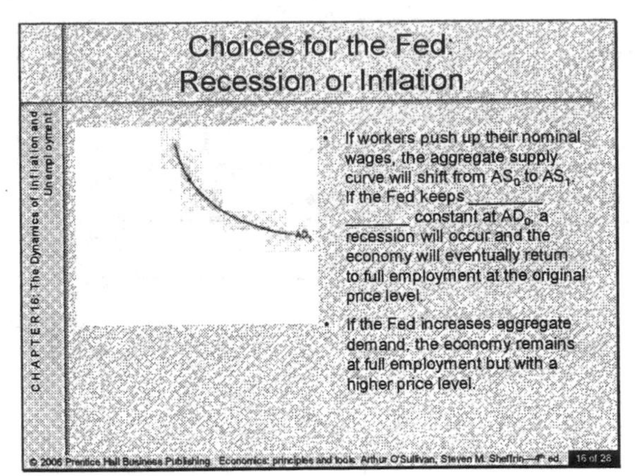

How the Credibility of a Nation's Central Bank Affects Inflation

- If the Fed is credible in its desire to fight inflation, it can deter the ________ sector from taking aggressive actions that drive up prices.
- With a credible central bank, a country can have lower inflation without experiencing extra unemployment. Central banks that have true independence from the rest of government will be more credible in their commitment to fight inflation.

CHAPTER 16: The Dynamics of Inflation and Unemployment

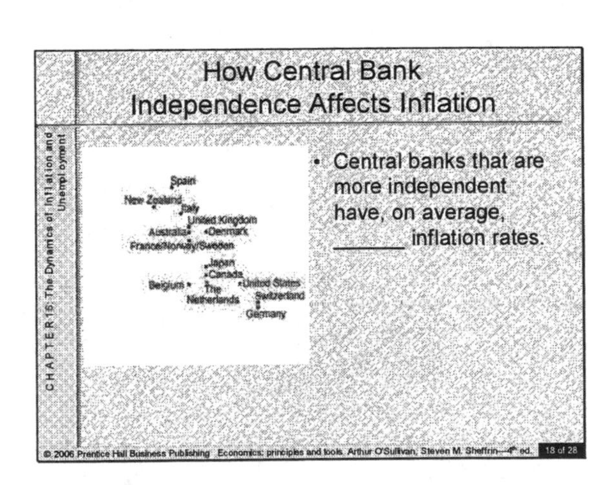

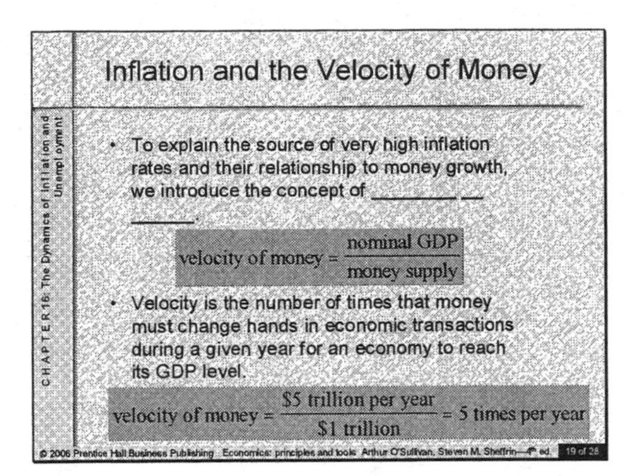

Inflation and the Velocity of Money

CHAPTER 16: The Dynamics of Inflation and Unemployment

- The equation of exchange, or ________ ________, links the money supply and velocity to nominal GDP:

money supply x velocity = nominal GDP

$$M \times V = P \times y$$

- If velocity is predictable, we can use the quantity equation and the supply of money to predict nominal GDP.

© 2006 Prentice Hall Business Publishing Economics: principles and tools Arthur O'Sullivan, Steven M. Sheffrin—4th ed. 20 of 28

Inflation and the Velocity of Money

CHAPTER 16: The Dynamics of Inflation and Unemployment

- The basic quantity equation can be used to derive a closely related formula for understanding inflation in the long run, called the ________ ________ **of the quantity equation**:

Growth rate of the money supply	+	Growth rate of velocity	=	Growth rate of prices	+	Growth rate of real output

- For example:

10%	+	0%	=	Growth rate of prices	+	3%

7%	=	Growth rate of prices	=	inflation

© 2006 Prentice Hall Business Publishing Economics: principles and tools Arthur O'Sullivan, Steven M. Sheffrin—4th ed. 21 of 28

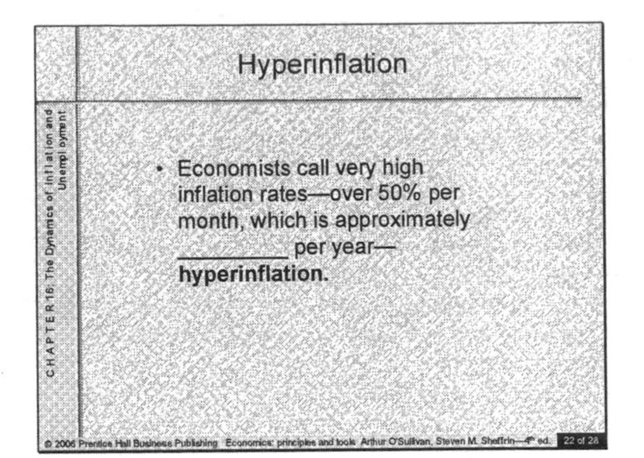

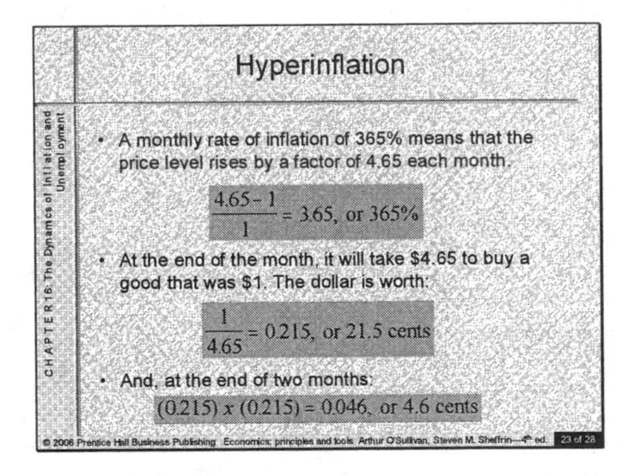

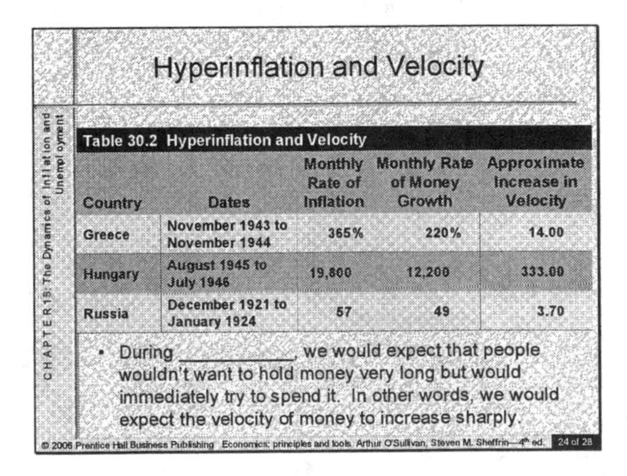

Table 30.2 Hyperinflation and Velocity

Country	Dates	Monthly Rate of Inflation	Monthly Rate of Money Growth	Approximate Increase in Velocity
Greece	November 1943 to November 1944	365%	220%	14.00
Hungary	August 1945 to July 1946	19,800	12,200	333.00
Russia	December 1921 to January 1924	57	49	3.70

Hyperinflations in the 1980s

- Hyperinflations have also occurred in recent times.

Table 30.3 Hyperinflations in the 1980s

		Rate of Inflation		Monthly Money
Country	Year	Yearly	Monthly	Growth Rate
Bolivia	1985	1,152,200%	118%	91%
Argentina	1989	302,200	95	93
Nicaragua	1988	975,500	115	66

© 2006 Prentice Hall Business Publishing Economics: principles and tools Arthur O'Sullivan, Steven M. Sheffrin—4th ed.

How Budget Deficits Lead to Hyperinflation

- Hyperinflation arises when governments allow the money supply to grow in order to finance the gap between government spending and revenues—the _______ _______.
- In principle, governments could use a mix of borrowing funds from the public and printing money to cover the deficit:

Government deficit = New borrowing from the public + New money created

© 2006 Prentice Hall Business Publishing Economics: principles and tools Arthur O'Sullivan, Steven M. Sheffrin—4th ed.

Budget Deficits and Hyperinflation

- Hyperinflations occur when governments cannot borrow from the public and are forced to print new money. To stop hyperinflation, it is necessary to eliminate the government deficit. Once the government stops printing money, the hyperinflation will end.
- Economists who emphasize the role that the supply of money plays in determining nominal income and inflation are called __________. Today, most economists agree with the monetarists that, in the long run, inflation is caused by growth in the money supply.

© 2006 Prentice Hall Business Publishing Economics: principles and tools Arthur O'Sullivan, Steven M. Sheffrin—4th ed.

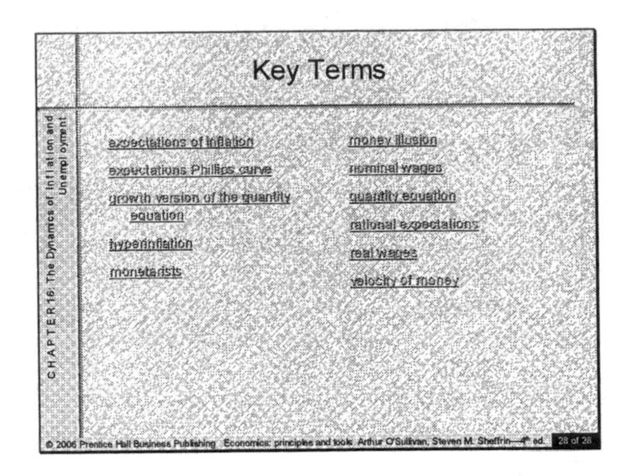
Key Terms
CHAPTER 16: The Dynamics of Inflation and Unemployment
expectations of inflation
expectations Phillips curve
growth version of the quantity equation
hyperinflation
monetarists
money illusion
nominal wages
quantity equation
rational expectations
real wages
velocity of money
© 2006 Prentice Hall Business Publishing Economics: principles and tools Arthur O'Sullivan, Steven M. Sheffrin—4th ed.
28 of 28

Current Issues in Macroeconomic Policy

- This chapter examines three key _______ issues in macroeconomics:
  1. Should the government balance its budget?
  2. Should the Federal Reserve just ______ inflation and not worry about output and unemployment?
  3. Should people be _____ on what they earn or what they spend?

© 2006 Prentice Hall Business Publishing Economics: principles and tools Arthur O'Sullivan, Steven M. Sheffrin—4th ed.

Should We Balance the Federal Budget?

- The purchase of goods and services by the government and the transfer payments (______ _______, welfare, and so on) it makes to its citizens are the **government's expenditures.**
- A **surplus** occurs when the government's revenues exceed its expenditures.
- The government runs a **deficit** when it spends more than it receives in revenues from either taxes or fees. The **government** ______ is the total of all of its yearly deficits.

© 2006 Prentice Hall Business Publishing Economics: principles and tools Arthur O'Sullivan, Steven M. Sheffrin—4th ed.

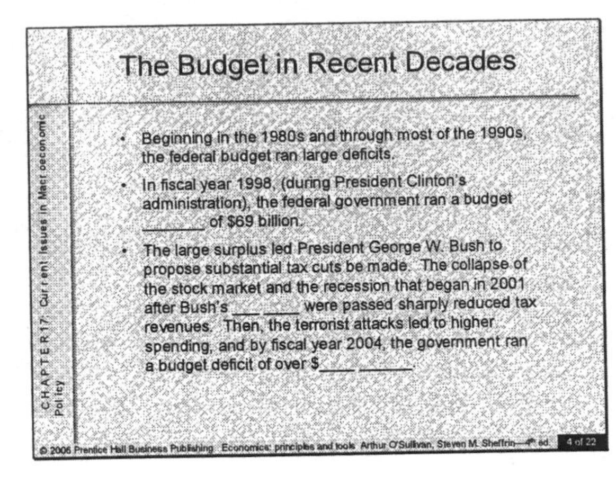
The Budget in Recent Decades
• Beginning in the 1980s and through most of the 1990s, the federal budget ran large deficits.
• In fiscal year 1998, (during President Clinton's administration), the federal government ran a budget _______ of $69 billion.
• The large surplus led President George W. Bush to propose substantial tax cuts be made. The collapse of the stock market and the recession that began in 2001 after Bush's ____ ____ were passed sharply reduced tax revenues. Then, the terrorist attacks led to higher spending, and by fiscal year 2004, the government ran a budget deficit of over $____ ______.
CHAPTER 17: Current Issues in Macroeconomic Policy
© 2006 Prentice Hall Business Publishing Economics: principles and tools Arthur O'Sullivan, Steven M. Sheffrin—4th ed.
4 of 22

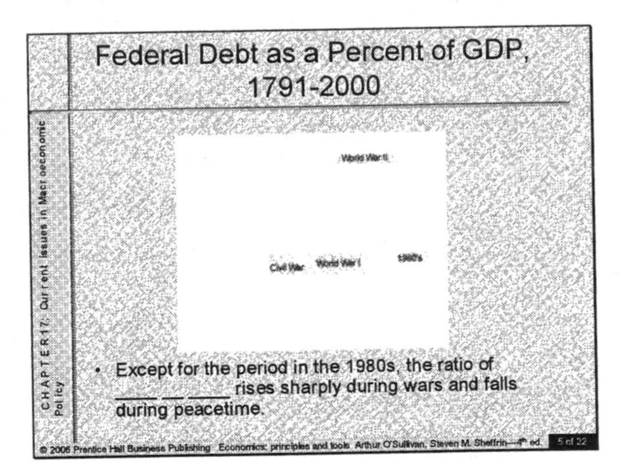
Federal Debt as a Percent of GDP, 1791-2000
World War II
Civil War
World War I
1980's
• Except for the period in the 1980s, the ratio of ____ __ ____ rises sharply during wars and falls during peacetime.
CHAPTER 17: Current Issues in Macroeconomic Policy
© 2006 Prentice Hall Business Publishing Economics: principles and tools Arthur O'Sullivan, Steven M. Sheffrin—4th ed.
5 of 22

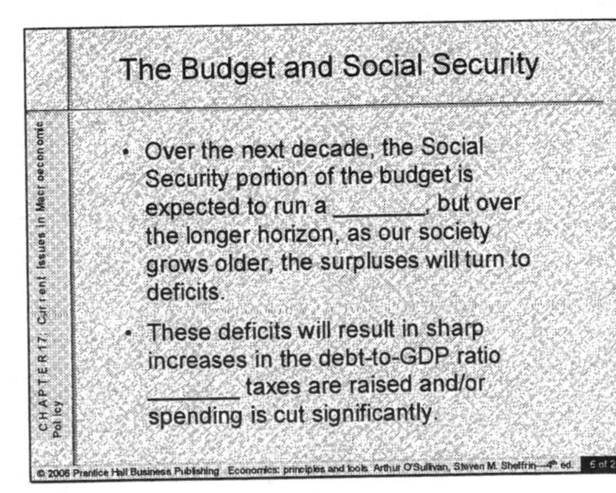
The Budget and Social Security
• Over the next decade, the Social Security portion of the budget is expected to run a _______, but over the longer horizon, as our society grows older, the surpluses will turn to deficits.
• These deficits will result in sharp increases in the debt-to-GDP ratio _______ taxes are raised and/or spending is cut significantly.
CHAPTER 17: Current Issues in Macroeconomic Policy
© 2006 Prentice Hall Business Publishing Economics: principles and tools Arthur O'Sullivan, Steven M. Sheffrin—4th ed.
6 of 22

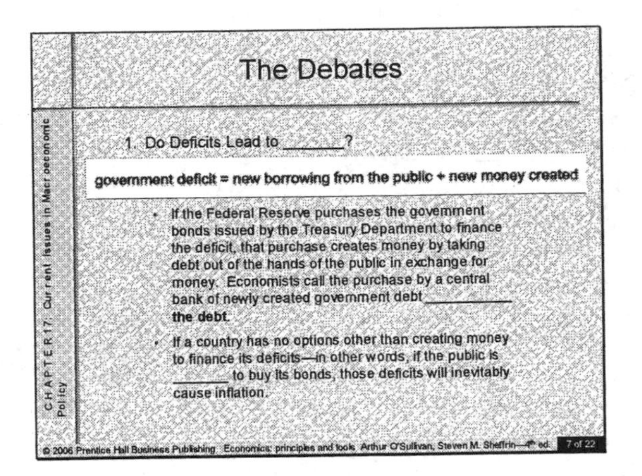

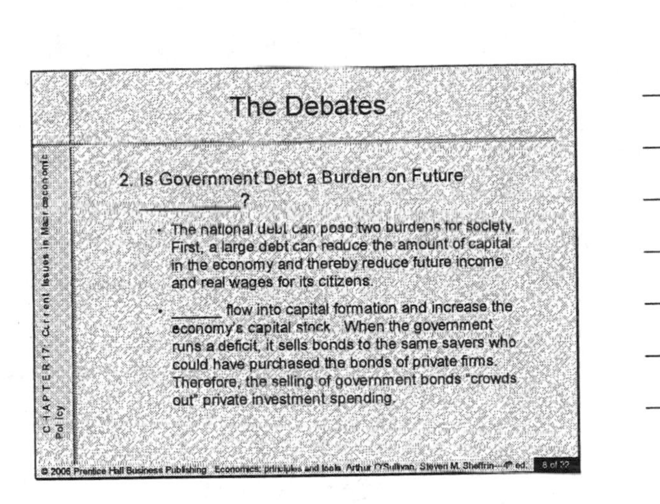

The Debates

2. Is Government Debt a Burden on Future Generations?

- Second, a large debt will mean that future generations will have to pay higher taxes to pay the ________ that accumulates on the debt.
- Economists who do not believe that government deficits impose a burden on society believe in the __________ **equivalence**, the proposition that it does not matter whether government expenditure is financed by taxes or by issuing debt because everyone understands that higher debt will result in higher taxes, so people save in anticipation of paying higher taxes in the future. In sum, the Ricardian equivalence requires that savings by the private sector increase when the deficit increases.

CHAPTER 17: Current Issues in Macroeconomic Policy

© 2006 Prentice Hall Business Publishing Economics: principles and tools Arthur O'Sullivan, Steven M. Sheffrin—4th ed. 9 of 22

The Debates

CHAPTER 17: Current Issues in Macroeconomic Policy

3. How Do Deficits Affect the Size of Government?
   - Nobel Laureate James _________ has argued that people are less aware of government deficits than the taxes they're forced to pay, and this inevitably will lead to higher government spending and bigger government.
   - More recent thinking suggests that deficits can be used strategically to actually reduce the growth of government. Lower taxes and higher deficits make it more difficult for other _________ to increase government spending.

The Debates

CHAPTER 17: Current Issues in Macroeconomic Policy

4. Can Deficits Be Good for an Economy?
   - Over ____ ______, deficits can help the economy to cope with shocks, such as oil price increases or a collapse in the stock market. They give the government some room to maneuver out of a recession.
   - Deficits can also play a role in tax smoothing. Professor Robert Barro of ________ University has argued that it is more efficient to keep tax rates relatively constant than to raise them sharply and then lower them later. Thus, by running deficits and only gradually raising taxes later to service the debt, we avoid creating excess distortions in the economy.

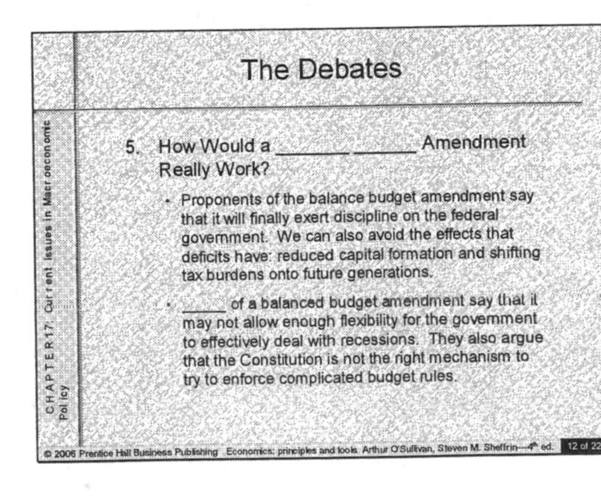

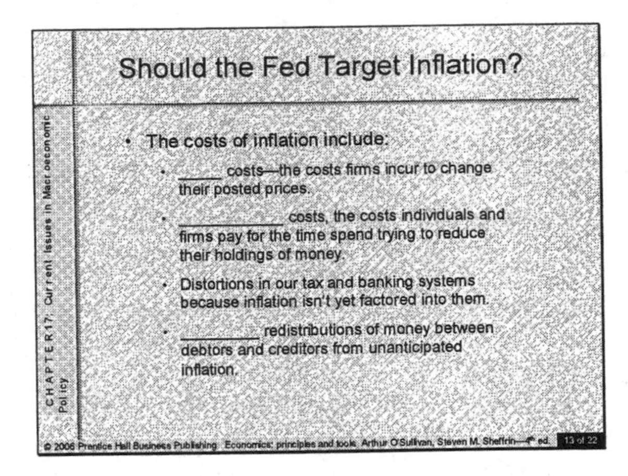

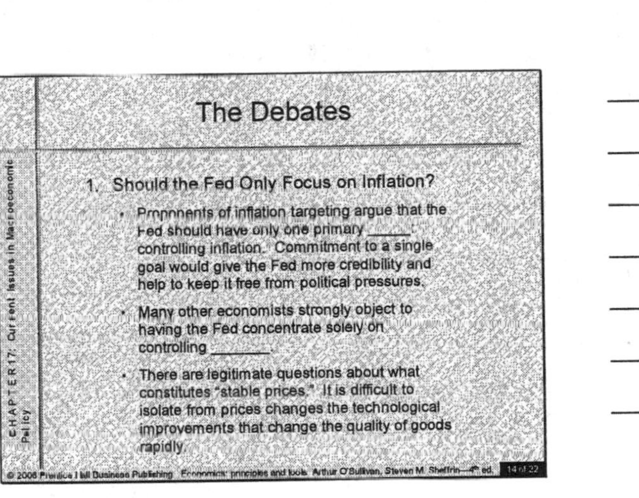

The Debates

1. Should the Fed Only Focus on Inflation?
   - Some economists like the idea of the Fed having to meet _______, such as to target the growth rate in nominal GDP and thereby both the growth in real GDP as well as the growth in prices (inflation).
   - Critics of stabilization policy believe that attempts to stabilize the economy have done more harm than good over the years by making fluctuations worse. Difficulties include lags, uncertainties about the strength and ______ of policies, and difficulties in estimating the natural rate of unemployment.

CHAPTER 17: Current Issues in Macroeconomic Policy

© 2006 Prentice Hall Business Publishing Economics: principles and tools Arthur O'Sullivan, Steven M. Sheffrin—4th ed.

The Debates

CHAPTER 17: Current Issues in Macroeconomic Policy

2. Who should set the inflation target?
   - In the United ________, it is ultimately the elected government that decides on the inflation target for the central bank.
   - In other countries, such as New Zealand, the central bank has the responsibility of "achieving and maintaining stability in the general level of prices" without any competing goals.
   - In the United States, the Fed has __________ power to use monetary policy to stabilize output as well as to fight inflation as it pleases. But changing the current system to give Congress and the president more power over monetary policy might lead to more inflation, not less.

© 2006 Prentice Hall Business Publishing Economics: principles and tools Arthur O'Sullivan, Steven M. Sheffrin—4th ed.

Should We Tax Consumption Rather than Income?

CHAPTER 17: Current Issues in Macroeconomic Policy

- The United States is a country with a ____ _______ rate. Colleges, welfare programs, and even the U.S. tax system discourage savings.
- Tax systems based on consumption do not penalize individuals who save. Sales taxes and value-added taxes are examples of _________ _____.
- The key feature of a **consumption tax** is that you do not face any additional taxes if you decide to save more of your income.
- In practice, the U.S. tax system is a ______ system: halfway between an income tax and a consumption tax.

© 2006 Prentice Hall Business Publishing Economics: principles and tools Arthur O'Sullivan, Steven M. Sheffrin—4th ed.

The Debates

CHAPTER 17: Current Issues in Macroeconomic Policy

1. Will Consumption Taxes Lead to More Savings?
   - It is clear that individuals will allocate their savings to tax-favored investments, such as ______, over investments that are not favored.
   - What is not clear if whether the funds are new savings—meaning reduced consumption—or merely _________ from other accounts.
   - Corporate income is _____ _____, first when it is earned by the corporation and again when it is paid out to shareholders. These corporate taxes may lead to less efficient investment because they result in capital flowing to sectors that do not suffer from double-taxation.

© 2006 Prentice Hall Business Publishing Economics: principles and tools Arthur O'Sullivan, Steven M. Sheffrin—4th ed.

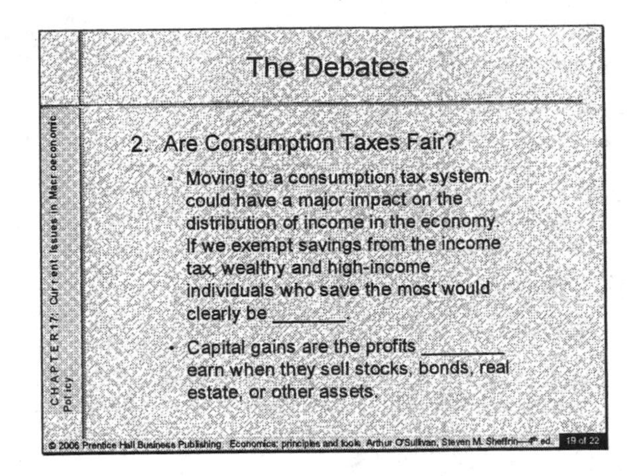

Share of Capital Gains by Income

CHAPTER17: Current Issues in Macroeconomic Policy

Tablo 31.1 Share of Capital Gains by Income, 1979-88

Income Class	Share of Capital Gains
$10,000-20,000	2.6%
$20,000-30,000	2.9
$30,000-40,000	4.4
$40,000-50,000	3.4
$50,000-75,000	9.0
$75,000-100,000	8.5
$100,000-200,000	15.7
$200,000 and over	56.8

- As shown on the table, taxpayers with annual incomes exceeding $200,000 earned over half of the economy's _____ _____ over this period. Obviously, capital assets are highly concentrated among the wealthy.

© 2006 Prentice Hall Business Publishing Economics: principles and tools Arthur O'Sullivan, Steven M. Sheffrin—4th ed.

The Debates

CHAPTER17: Current Issues in Macroeconomic Policy

2. Are Consumption Taxes Fair?
   - If capital gains and other types of _____ income were not taxed, the government would have to raise tax rates on everyone to maintain the same level of spending.
   - Certain types of taxes, however, would not cause sharp changes in the relative tax burdens. The "flat tax" designed by Robert E Hall of Stanford University and Alvin Rabushka of the Hoover Institute brings the personal income tax and corporate income tax into a single, _______ system. The tax would allow a deduction for investment spending and only extraordinary gains would be taxed.

© 2006 Prentice Hall Business Publishing Economics: principles and tools Arthur O'Sullivan, Steven M. Sheffrin—4th ed.

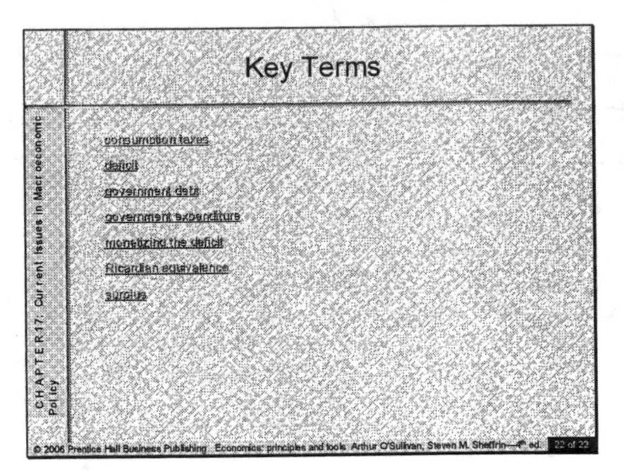
Key Terms
consumption taxes
deficit
government debt
government expenditure
monetizing the deficit
Ricardian equivalence
surplus
CHAPTER 17: Current Issues in Macroeconomic Policy
© 2006 Prentice Hall Business Publishing Economics: principles and tools Arthur O'Sullivan, Steven M. Sheffrin—4th ed.
22 of 22

Benefits from Specialization and Trade

CHAPTER 18: International Trade and Public Policy

- If a nation produced everything it consumed, it would not ______ on any other nation for its livelihood.
- Although self-sufficiency sounds appealing, countries are better off if they ________ in the production of some products and trade some of them to other countries.
- Specialization and _____ are concepts based on the principle of opportunity cost.

PRINCIPLE *of Opportunity Cost*
The opportunity cost of something is what you sacrifice to get it.

© 2006 Prentice Hall Business Publishing Economics: principles and tools Arthur O'Sullivan, Steven M. Sheffrin—4th ed.

Benefits from Specialization and Trade

CHAPTER 18: International Trade and Public Policy

Table 32.1 Output and Opportunity Cost

	Shirtland	Chipland
Shirts produced per day	108	120
Chips produced per day	36	120
Opportunity cost of shirts	1/3 chip	1 chip
Opportunity cost of chips	3 shirts	1 shirt

- The **production possibilities frontier** shows the possible _________ of two goods that can be produced by an economy, assuming that all resources are fully employed.

© 2006 Prentice Hall Business Publishing Economics: principles and tools Arthur O'Sullivan, Steven M. Sheffrin—4th ed.

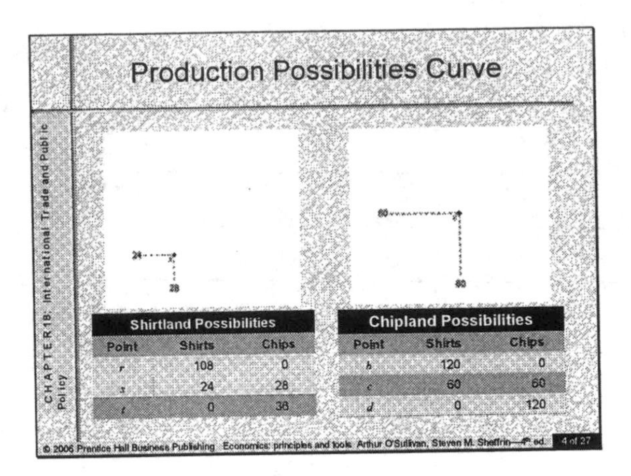
Production Possibilities Curve
CHAPTER 18: International Trade and Public Policy
24
28
60
60
Shirtland Possibilities
Point Shirts Chips
r 108 0
s 24 28
t 0 36
Chipland Possibilities
Point Shirts Chips
b 120 0
c 60 60
d 0 120
© 2006 Prentice Hall Business Publishing Economics: principles and tools Arthur O'Sullivan, Steven M. Sheffrin—4th ed.
4 of 27

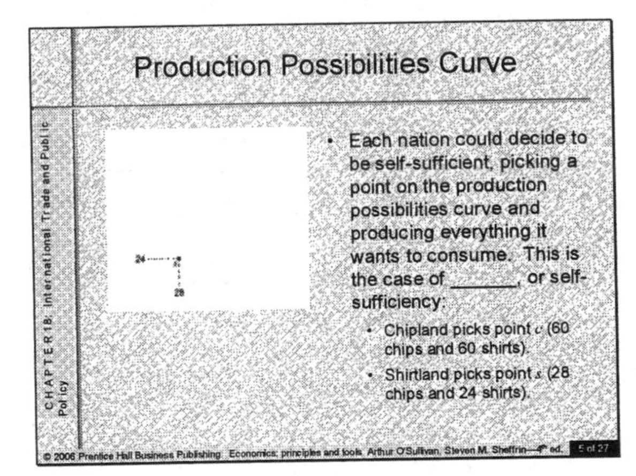
Production Possibilities Curve
CHAPTER 18: International Trade and Public Policy
24
28
Each nation could decide to be self-sufficient, picking a point on the production possibilities curve and producing everything it wants to consume. This is the case of ______, or self-sufficiency:
Chipland picks point c (60 chips and 60 shirts).
Shirtland picks point s (28 chips and 24 shirts).
© 2006 Prentice Hall Business Publishing Economics: principles and tools Arthur O'Sullivan, Steven M. Sheffrin—4th ed.
5 of 27

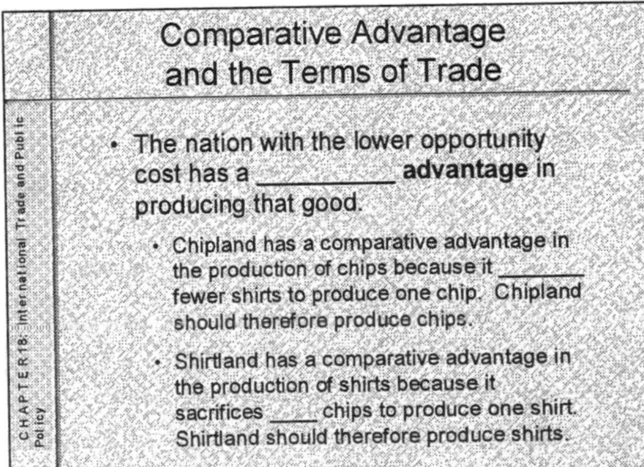
Comparative Advantage and the Terms of Trade
CHAPTER 18: International Trade and Public Policy
The nation with the lower opportunity cost has a __________ advantage in producing that good.
Chipland has a comparative advantage in the production of chips because it _______ fewer shirts to produce one chip. Chipland should therefore produce chips.
Shirtland has a comparative advantage in the production of shirts because it sacrifices ____ chips to produce one shirt. Shirtland should therefore produce shirts.
© 2006 Prentice Hall Business Publishing Economics: principles and tools Arthur O'Sullivan, Steven M. Sheffrin—4th ed.
6 of 27

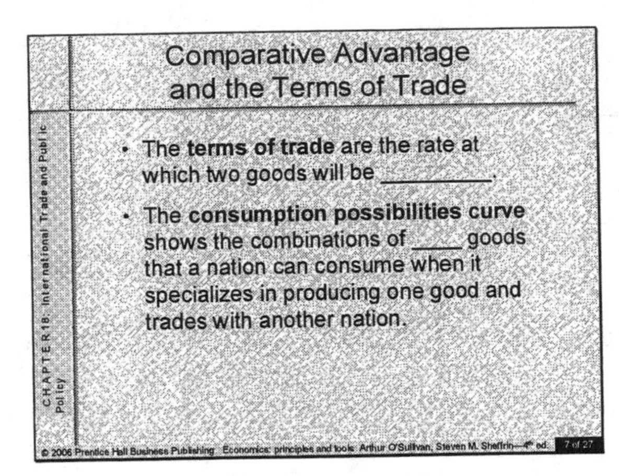
Comparative Advantage and the Terms of Trade
The terms of trade are the rate at which two goods will be ________.
The consumption possibilities curve shows the combinations of ____ goods that a nation can consume when it specializes in producing one good and trades with another nation.
CHAPTER 18: International Trade and Public Policy
© 2006 Prentice Hall Business Publishing Economics: principles and tools Arthur O'Sullivan, Steven M. Sheffrin—4th ed.
7 of 27

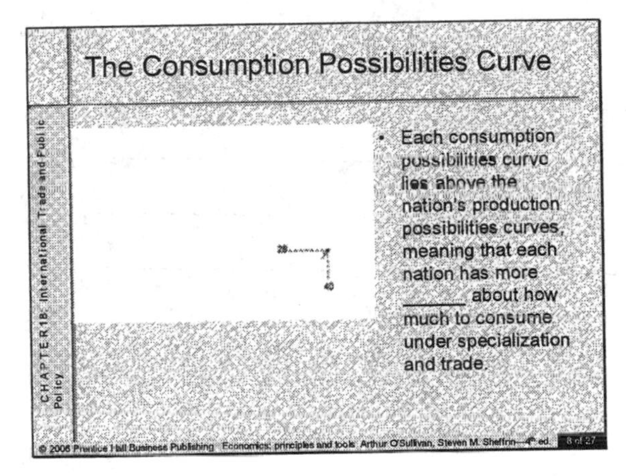
The Consumption Possibilities Curve
Each consumption possibilities curve lies above the nation's production possibilities curves, meaning that each nation has more ______ about how much to consume under specialization and trade.
28
40
CHAPTER 18: International Trade and Public Policy
© 2006 Prentice Hall Business Publishing Economics: principles and tools Arthur O'Sullivan, Steven M. Sheffrin—4th ed.
8 of 27

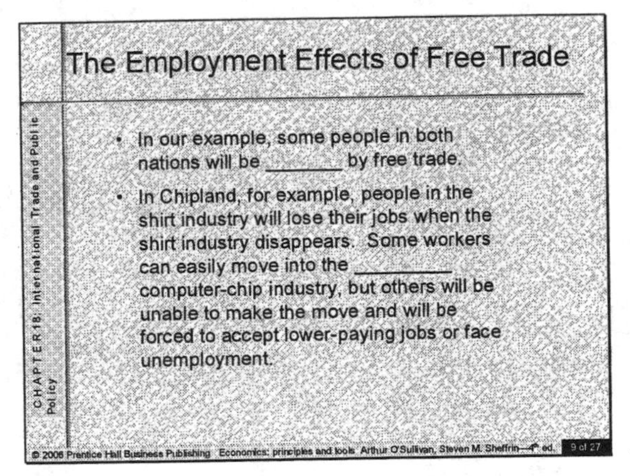
The Employment Effects of Free Trade
In our example, some people in both nations will be _______ by free trade.
In Chipland, for example, people in the shirt industry will lose their jobs when the shirt industry disappears. Some workers can easily move into the _________ computer-chip industry, but others will be unable to make the move and will be forced to accept lower-paying jobs or face unemployment.
CHAPTER 18: International Trade and Public Policy
© 2006 Prentice Hall Business Publishing Economics: principles and tools Arthur O'Sullivan, Steven M. Sheffrin—4th ed.
9 of 27

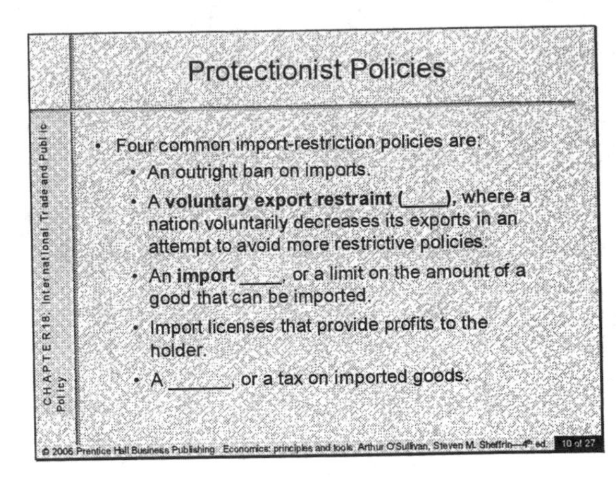

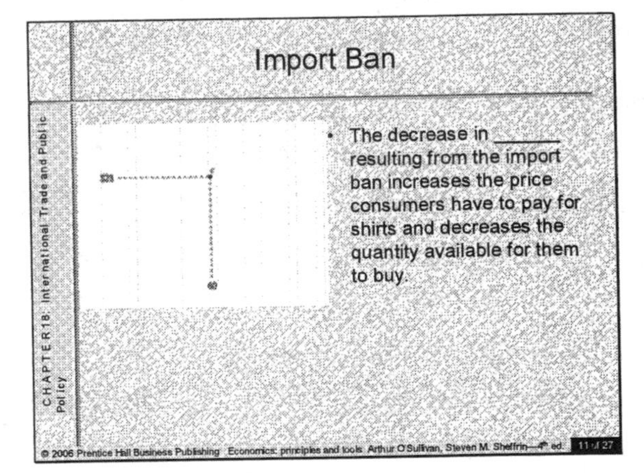

Quotas and Voluntary Export Restraints

CHAPTER 18: International Trade and Public Policy

- An import quota is a ________ policy that falls between free trade and an outright ban: Imports are cut but not eliminated. Import quotas are illegal under international trading rules.
- To get around these rules, an exporting country will sometimes agree to a voluntary export restraint (VER). A VER is similar to an import ban. Like a quota, a VER increases the price of the restricted good, making it more feasible for domestic firms to _________ in the market.

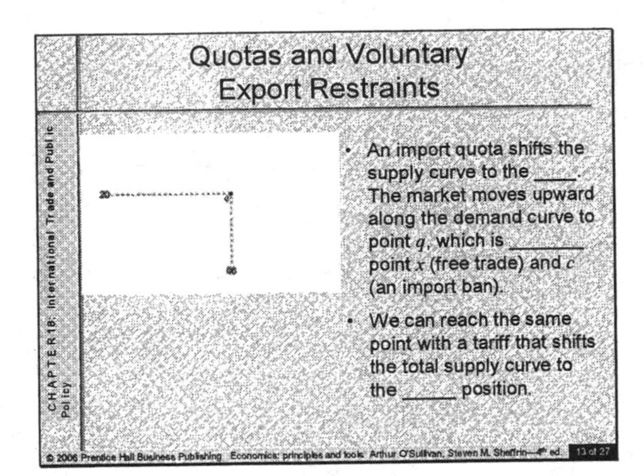
Quotas and Voluntary Export Restraints
CHAPTER 18: International Trade and Public Policy
20
• An import quota shifts the supply curve to the ____. The market moves upward along the demand curve to point q, which is ______ point x (free trade) and c (an import ban).
• We can reach the same point with a tariff that shifts the total supply curve to the _____ position.
© 2006 Prentice Hall Business Publishing Economics: principles and tools Arthur O'Sullivan, Steven M. Sheffrin—4th ed.
13 of 27

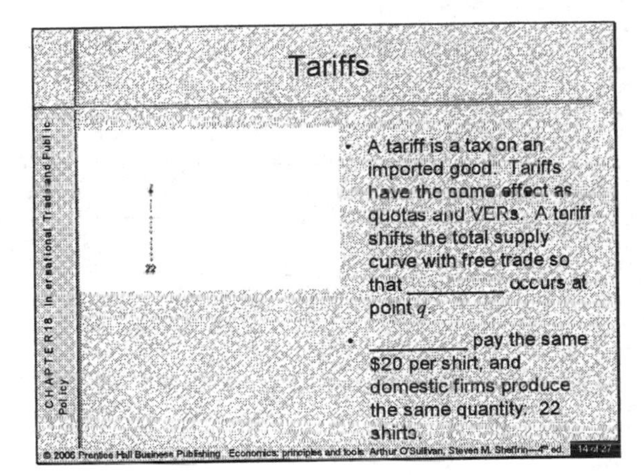
Tariffs
CHAPTER 18: International Trade and Public Policy
22
• A tariff is a tax on an imported good. Tariffs have the same effect as quotas and VERs. A tariff shifts the total supply curve with free trade so that _________ occurs at point q.
• _________ pay the same $20 per shirt, and domestic firms produce the same quantity: 22 shirts.
© 2006 Prentice Hall Business Publishing Economics: principles and tools Arthur O'Sullivan, Steven M. Sheffrin—4th ed.
14 of 27

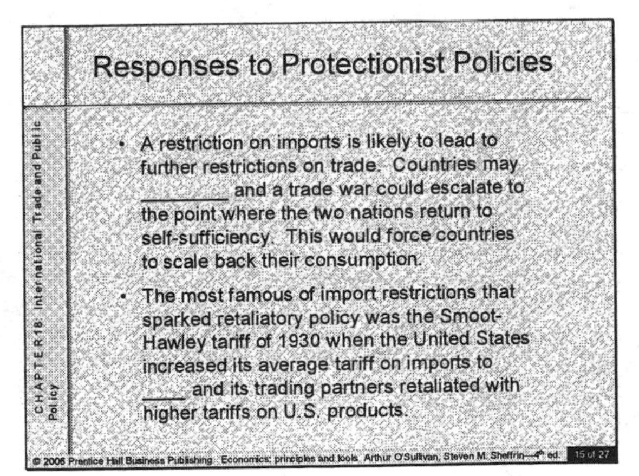
Responses to Protectionist Policies
CHAPTER 18: International Trade and Public Policy
• A restriction on imports is likely to lead to further restrictions on trade. Countries may ________ and a trade war could escalate to the point where the two nations return to self-sufficiency. This would force countries to scale back their consumption.
• The most famous of import restrictions that sparked retaliatory policy was the Smoot-Hawley tariff of 1930 when the United States increased its average tariff on imports to ____ and its trading partners retaliated with higher tariffs on U.S. products.
© 2006 Prentice Hall Business Publishing Economics: principles and tools Arthur O'Sullivan, Steven M. Sheffrin—4th ed.
15 of 27

Notetaker152

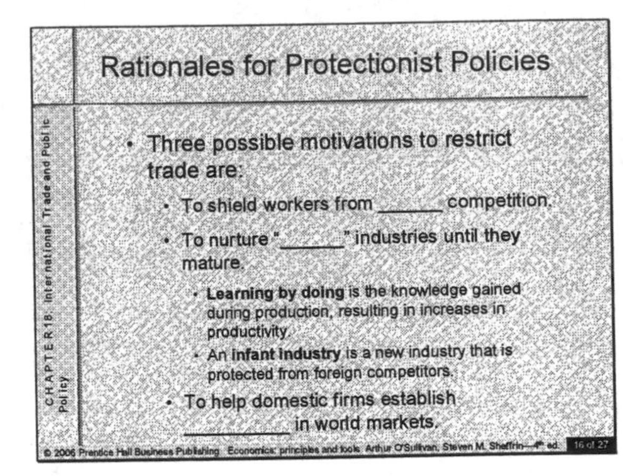

A Brief History of International Tariff and Trade Agreements

CHAPTER 18: International Trade and Public Policy

- The first major trade agreement following World War II was the General Agreement on Tariffs and Trade (_____).
- There have been nine rounds of negotiations, resulting in progressively _____ _____ for the member nations.
- In 1995, the World Trade Organization (___) was formed to enforce GATT and other international trade agreements.

© 2006 Prentice Hall Business Publishing Economics: principles and tools Arthur O'Sullivan, Steven M. Sheffrin—4th ed.

A Brief History of International Tariff and Trade Agreements

CHAPTER 18: International Trade and Public Policy

- Other nations have formed trade associations to lower trade barriers and promote international trade:
  - The North American Free Trade Agreement (______) between Canada, Mexico, and the United States.
  - The ________ Union (EU), which today includes close to 20 countries.
  - The leaders of 18 _____ nations have formed the Asian Pacific Economic Cooperation (APEC).

© 2006 Prentice Hall Business Publishing Economics: principles and tools Arthur O'Sullivan, Steven M. Sheffrin—4th ed.

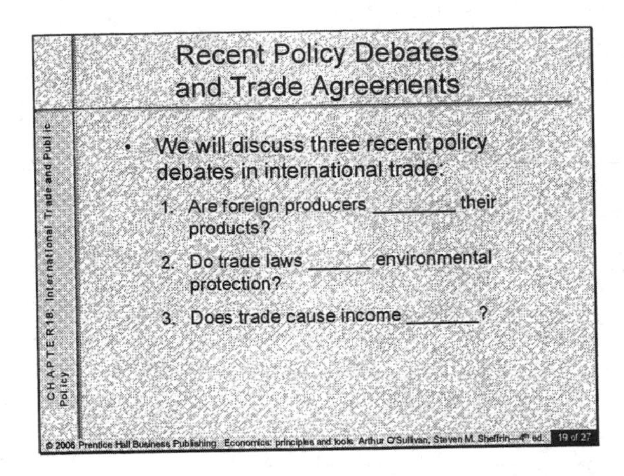

Are Foreign Producers Dumping Their Products?

- A firm is **dumping** when the price it charges in a foreign market is either lower than the price it charges in its home market or lower than its production _____.
- Dumping is ____ under international trade agreements; hundreds of cases of alleged dumping are presented to WTO authorities each year.

CHAPTER 18: International Trade and Public Policy

© 2006 Prentice Hall Business Publishing Economics: principles and tools Arthur O'Sullivan, Steven M. Sheffrin—4th ed. 20 of 27

Are Foreign Producers Dumping Their Products?

- Charging a lower price in the foreign market is a form of **price discrimination**—a ________ that maximizes profit.
- A second reason for dumping is ________ **pricing**: cutting prices in an attempt to drive rival firms out of business. The predatory firm sets its price below its production cost.

CHAPTER 18: International Trade and Public Policy

© 2006 Prentice Hall Business Publishing Economics: principles and tools Arthur O'Sullivan, Steven M. Sheffrin—4th ed. 21 of 27

Are Foreign Producers Dumping Their Products?

- Many economists are ________ about how frequently predatory pricing actually occurs versus price discrimination; they suspect that many nations use their antidumping laws as protectionist policies in disguise.
- Professor Thomas Prusa of Rutgers University has studied ___________ and found that it is a potent weapon for protecting domestic industries.

© 2006 Prentice Hall Business Publishing Economics: principles and tools Arthur O'Sullivan, Steven M. Sheffrin—4th ed.

Do Trade Laws Inhibit Environmental Protection?

- Starting in the early 1990s, environmentalists began to question whether policies that ________ trade could harm the environment.
- Under current WTO rules, a country can adopt any environmental standard it chooses, as long as it does not ___________ against foreign producers.
- The United States cannot ban imported goods produced by factories that generate air or water ________ in other countries.

© 2006 Prentice Hall Business Publishing Economics: principles and tools Arthur O'Sullivan, Steven M. Sheffrin—4th ed.

Do Trade Laws Inhibit Environmental Protection?

- Nations that use trade restrictions to pursue environmental goals will encounter _________ because WTO rules mean that a nation can pursue its environmental goals only within its borders.
- In recent years, a new breed of trade _______ have erupted revolving around social problems and the role of the government in trying to solve them.
- As a world trading community, we will have to decide at what point we allow national policy concerns to override principles of _____ _____.

© 2006 Prentice Hall Business Publishing Economics: principles and tools Arthur O'Sullivan, Steven M. Sheffrin—4th ed.

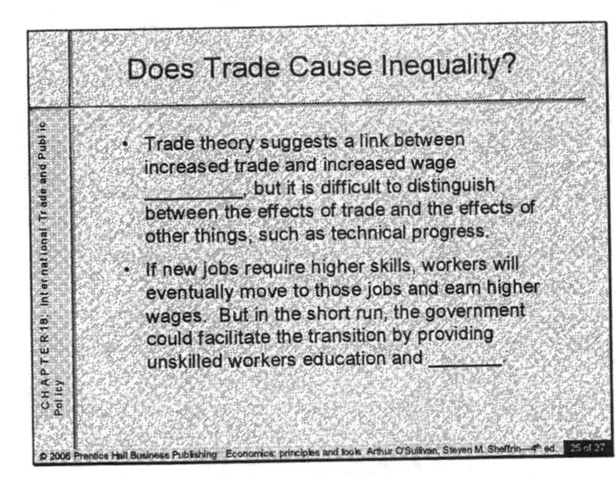

Why Do People Protest Against Free Trade?

- Trade and specialization mean that individuals and nations must surrender some of their independence and __________.
- By not producing precisely what we consume, we become dependent on others to trade. By cooperating with other nations, we need to develop agreed-upon rules that, at times, limit our own _______.

CHAPTER 18: International Trade and Public Policy

© 2006 Prentice Hall Business Publishing Economics: principles and tools Arthur O'Sullivan, Steven M. Sheffrin—4th ed. 26 of 27

Key Terms

- autarky
- comparative advantage
- consumption possibilities curve
- dumping
- import quota
- infant industry
- learning by doing
- production possibilities curve
- tariff
- terms of trade
- voluntary export restraint (VER)
- price discrimination
- predatory pricing

CHAPTER 18: International Trade and Public Policy

© 2006 Prentice Hall Business Publishing Economics: principles and tools Arthur O'Sullivan, Steven M. Sheffrin—4th ed. 27 of 27

Notetaker156

How Exchange Rates Are Determined

CHAPTER 19: The World of International Finance

- The **exchange rate** is defined as the rate at which we can exchange one ________ for another.
- Fluctuations in the exchange rate can have a huge impact on what countries imports, exports, and the overall trade _______.

© 2006 Prentice Hall Business Publishing Economics: principles and tools Arthur O'Sullivan, Steven M. Sheffrin—4th ed.

What Are Exchange Rates?

CHAPTER 19: The World of International Finance

- An increase in the value of a currency is called an ___________. When the dollar appreciates against the yen, one dollar will purchase more yen.
- A ___________ is a reduction in the value of a currency.
- If one currency appreciates, the other must depreciate.

© 2006 Prentice Hall Business Publishing Economics: principles and tools Arthur O'Sullivan, Steven M. Sheffrin—4th ed.

What Are Exchange Rates?

- If a watch sells for 300 Swiss francs and the exchange rate between francs and dollars is 2 francs per dollar, the watch would cost you $150:

  300 francs/2 francs per dollar = $150

- If the exchange rate is 3 francs per dollar, the watch would cost only $_____.

CHAPTER 19: The World of International Finance

© 2006 Prentice Hall Business Publishing Economics: principles and tools Arthur O'Sullivan, Steven M. Sheffrin—4th ed.

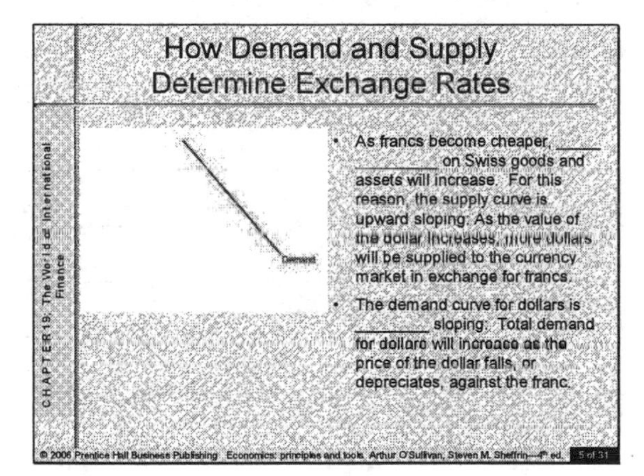

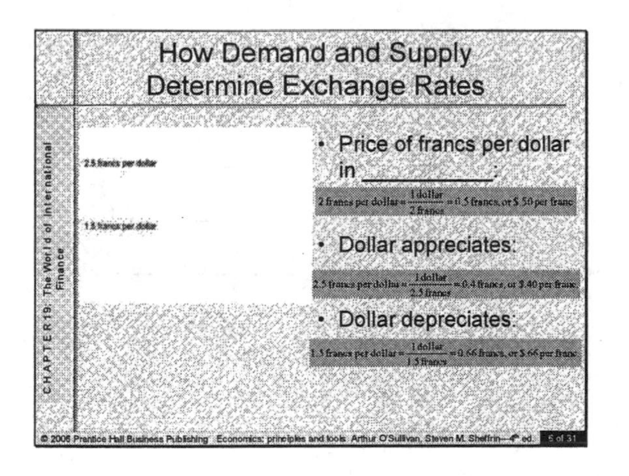

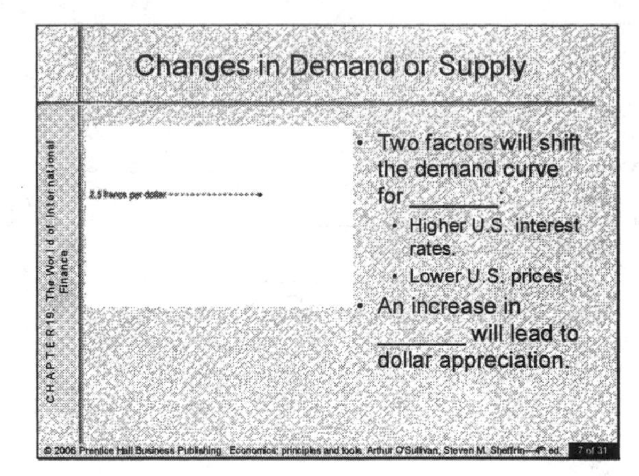

Changes in Demand or Supply

1.5 francs per dollar

- The same two factors that shift the demand curve will ______ the supply curve for dollars to the right:
  - Lower U.S. interest rates.
  - Higher U.S. prices
- An increase in ______ will lead to dollar depreciation.

CHAPTER 19: The World of International Finance

© 2006 Prentice Hall Business Publishing Economics: principles and tools Arthur O'Sullivan, Steven M. Sheffrin—4th ed.

Real Exchange Rates and Purchasing Power Parity

- We need to adjust the exchange rate determined in the foreign exchange market to take into account changes in ____. This is an application of the real-nominal principle:

Real-Nominal PRINCIPLE
What matters to people is the real value of money or income—its purchasing power—not the "face" value of money or income.

- The **real exchange rate** is defined as the price of all U.S. goods and services ______ to all foreign goods and services, expressed in a common currency.

$$\text{Real exchange rate} = \frac{\text{exchange rate x price index}}{\text{foreign price index}}$$

CHAPTER 19: The World of International Finance

© 2006 Prentice Hall Business Publishing Economics: principles and tools Arthur O'Sullivan, Steven M. Sheffrin—4th ed.

Real Exchange Rates and Purchasing Power Parity

CHAPTER 19: The World of International Finance

$$\text{Real exchange rate} = \frac{\text{exchange rate x price index}}{\text{foreign price index}}$$

- We measure the real exchange rate by expressing U.S. prices in foreign currency and _________ them to foreign prices.
- An increase in U.S. prices, appreciation of the dollar, or a decrease in _____ prices will raise the real exchange rate.
- The real exchange rate takes into account changes in a country's prices over time because of _______.

© 2006 Prentice Hall Business Publishing Economics: principles and tools Arthur O'Sullivan, Steven M. Sheffrin—4th ed. 10 of 31

Real Exchange Rates and Purchasing Power Parity

CHAPTER 19: The World of International Finance

- The tendency for easily tradable goods to sell at the same price when expressed in a common currency is known as the _____ __ ____ _____.
- According to one theory of how market exchange rates are determined, market exchange rates simply reflect differences in the overall price levels between countries. This theory is known as **purchasing power** ______.

© 2006 Prentice Hall Business Publishing Economics: principles and tools Arthur O'Sullivan, Steven M. Sheffrin—4th ed. 12 of 31

Real Exchange Rates and Purchasing Power Parity

Table 33.1 Big Mac Pricing Around the World Versus Actual Exchange Rates

Country	Price of a Big Mac in Local Currency	Price of a Big Mac in Dollars	Predicted Purchasing Power Exchange Rate Based on Big Mac Pricing (Foreign Currency per U.S. Dollar)	Actual Exchange Rate (Foreign Currency per Dollar)
United States	2.80 dollars	$2.80		
United Kingdom	1.88 pounds	$3.45	0.67	0.54
Hong Kong	12.0 HK dollars	$1.55	4.29	7.76
Switzerland	6.29 Swiss francs	$5.11	2.25	1.23
Mexico	23.9 pesos	$2.21	8.53	10.8
Japan	262 yen	$2.47	93.6	106

© 2006 Prentice Hall Business Publishing Economics: principles and tools Arthur O'Sullivan, Steven M. Sheffrin—4th ed.

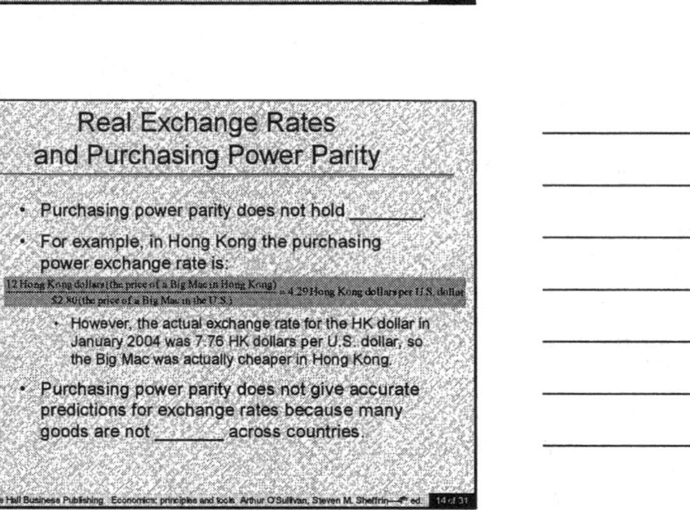

The Current Account and the Capital Account

- A country's ______ **account** is the sum of its net exports (exports minus imports), net income received from investments abroad, and net transfer payments from abroad.
- If a country has a positive current account, we say that its current account is in ______, and if it is negative, we say that its current account is in deficit.

© 2006 Prentice Hall Business Publishing Economics: principles and tools Arthur O'Sullivan, Steven M. Sheffrin—4th ed.

The Current Account and the Capital Account

- A country's _______ **account** transactions include all the purchases and sales of existing assets (stocks, bonds, real estate) by the private sector and the government.
- The capital account is defined as the value of the country's ___ sales (sales less purchases) of assets.
- If the value on the capital account is positive, we say that the country has a surplus on the capital account. Similarly, if the value on the capital account is _______, we say that it has a deficit on the capital account.

© 2006 Prentice Hall Business Publishing Economics: principles and tools Arthur O'Sullivan, Steven M. Sheffrin—4th ed.

Rules for Calculating the Capital and Current Account

- Any action that gives rise to a _______ for foreign currency is a deficit item on the current account or on the capital account.
- Any action that gives rise to a _____ of foreign currency is a surplus item on the current account or on the capital account.

© 2006 Prentice Hall Business Publishing Economics: principles and tools Arthur O'Sullivan, Steven M. Sheffrin—4th ed.

The Current Account and the Capital Account

- Applying this rule to the current account with the point of view of the U.S., we have:

U.S. current account surplus = U.S. exports - U.S. imports
+ net income from foreign investments
+ net transfers from abroad

- Applying for the capital account, we have:

U.S. capital account surplus = foreign purchases of U.S. assets
− U.S. purchases of foreign assets

- The current account and the capital account of a country are linked by a very important _______:

current account + capital account = 0

© 2006 Prentice Hall Business Publishing Economics: principles and tools Arthur O'Sullivan, Steven M. Sheffrin—4th ed.

The Current Account and the Capital Account

- If a country runs a current account surplus—it's exporting more than it's importing, in other words, it acquires foreign exchange.
- The ____ **international investment position** of a country equals its domestic holdings of foreign assets minus the foreign holdings of domestic assets. When this position is negative, the country is a net debtor.

U.S. Current Account and Capital Account, 2002 (billions)

Table 33.2 U.S. Current Account and Capital Account, 2002 (billions)	
Current account	
Goods	-482
Services	65
Net Transfers	-59
Net investment income	-4
Total on Current account	-480
Capital account	
Increase in U.S. holdings abroad	-179
Increases in foreign holding in U.S.	707
Total on Capital account	528
Statistical discrepancy	-48
Sum of current account, capital account, and statistical discrepancy	

Fixing the Exchange Rate

- When a country's exchange rate depreciates, imports become more expensive and the cost of living in that country increases. At the same time, exports will increase. Sometimes, __________ try to prevent the effects of appreciation or depreciation.
- Efforts by governments to influence the exchange rate are called **foreign exchange rate** _________. Governments have to affect the demand or supply for their currency.

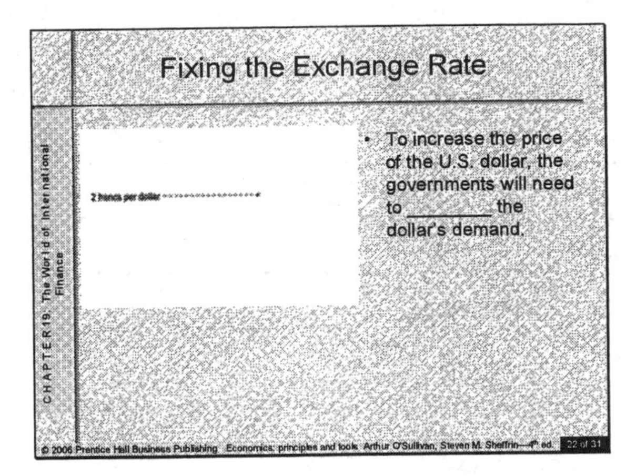

Fixed Versus Flexible Exchange Rates

- Currency systems in which governments try to keep constant the values of their currencies against one another are called ______ **exchange rate systems**.
- After World War II, the countries of the world operated under a fixed exchange rate system known as ______ ______, whereby all countries fixed or pegged their currencies against the U.S. dollar.

CHAPTER 19: The World of International Finance

© 2006 Prentice Hall Business Publishing Economics: principles and tools Arthur O'Sullivan, Steven M. Sheffrin—4th ed. 23 of 31

Fixed Exchange Rates

- In a fixed exchange rate system, a **balance of payments deficit** will occur whenever there is a deficit in the current account that is not _______ by net sales of assets to foreigners by the private sector.
- This is a situation in which the supply of a country's currency exceeds the demand for the currency at the current exchange rate. To _________ the currency from depreciating, the government would have to sell foreign currency and buy its own currency.

CHAPTER 19: The World of International Finance

© 2006 Prentice Hall Business Publishing Economics: principles and tools Arthur O'Sullivan, Steven M. Sheffrin—4th ed. 24 of 31

Fixed Exchange Rates

- An excess demand for a country's currency at the fixed exchange rate is known as a **balance of payments surplus**. Without government intervention, the country's currency will rise in value. To prevent its currency from appreciating, the government will have to ____ foreign currency and sell its own.

© 2006 Prentice Hall Business Publishing Economics: principles and tools Arthur O'Sullivan, Steven M. Sheffrin—4th ed.

Fixed Exchange Rates

- A country that faces a balance of payments deficit can lower the value at which the currency is pegged to increase its net exports; this is called a ____________.
- Conversely, a country that faces a balance of payments surplus can increase the value at which its currency is pegged and reduce its net exports; this is called a __________.

© 2006 Prentice Hall Business Publishing Economics: principles and tools Arthur O'Sullivan, Steven M. Sheffrin—4th ed.

The U.S. Experience with Fixed and Flexible Exchange Rates

- The Bretton Woods system lasted until the early 1970s when the world abandoned it and went to the current system—a ______ **exchange rate system**—in which free markets primarily determine exchange rates.
- Fixed exchange rate systems require countries to maintain similar economic policies—especially to maintain _______ inflation rates and interest rates.

© 2006 Prentice Hall Business Publishing Economics: principles and tools Arthur O'Sullivan, Steven M. Sheffrin—4th ed.

Exchange Rate Systems Today

- The flexible exchange rate system has worked well enough since the breakdown of Bretton Woods. It has seamlessly managed many diverse situations.
- One way to avoid some of the difficulties of fixing exchange rates between countries is to abolish individual currencies and establish a ______ currency.
- European countries adopted a common currency, named the ____, and established a single central bank to control its supply.

© 2006 Prentice Hall Business Publishing Economics: principles and tools Arthur O'Sullivan, Steven M. Sheffrin—4th ed.

Managing Financial Crises

- In vast ______ capital markets, funds can move quickly from country to country, and economic policies sometimes do not keep pace with changing political and economic developments.
- It can be extremely ______ to maintain a fixed exchange rate in this environment.
- The countries of the world are searching for a reliable set of rules and institutional mechanisms that can avoid and _____ the spread of financial crises.

© 2006 Prentice Hall Business Publishing Economics: principles and tools Arthur O'Sullivan, Steven M. Sheffrin—4th ed.

Managing Financial Crises

- As world capital markets continue to grow, governments throughout the world will almost surely be tested by new and often ___________ financial crises.
- They will need to anticipate and ______ to rapid changes in the economic and political environment to maintain a stable financial environment for world trade.

© 2006 Prentice Hall Business Publishing Economics: principles and tools Arthur O'Sullivan, Steven M. Sheffrin—4th ed.

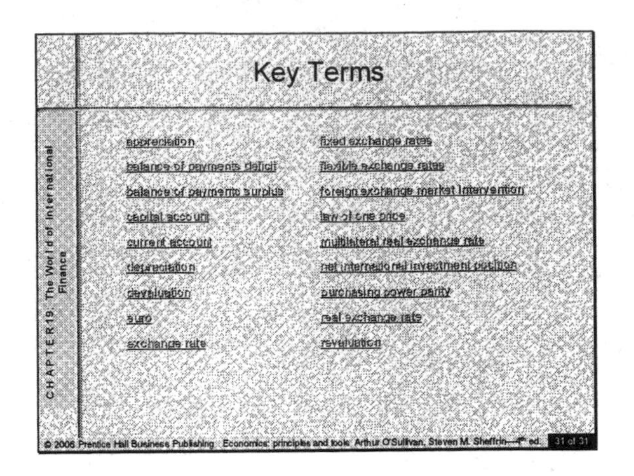
Key Terms
appreciation
balance of payments deficit
balance of payments surplus
capital account
current account
depreciation
devaluation
euro
exchange rate
fixed exchange rates
flexible exchange rates
foreign exchange market intervention
law of one price
multilateral real exchange rate
net international investment position
purchasing power parity
real exchange rate
revaluation
CHAPTER 19: The World of International Finance
© 2006 Prentice Hall Business Publishing Economics: principles and tools Arthur O'Sullivan, Steven M. Sheffrin—4th ed.
31 of 31